Guidance notes and flow charts for the

Professional Services Contract

This contract should be used for the appointment of a supplier to provide professional services

An NEC document

June 2005

OGC endorsement of NEC3

OGC advises public sector procurers that the form of contract used has to be selected according to the objectives of the project, aiming to satisfy the *Achieving Excellence in Construction* (AEC) principles.

This edition of the NEC (NEC3) complies fully with the AEC principles. OGC recommends the use of NEC3 by public sector construction procurers on their construction projects.

Office of Government Commerce

NEC is a division of Thomas Telford Ltd, which is a wholly owned subsidiary of the Institution of Civil Engineers (ICE), the owner and developer of the NEC.

The NEC is a family of standard contracts, each of which has these characteristics:

- Its use stimulates good management of the relationship between the two parties to the contract and, hence, of the work included in the contract.

- It can be used in a wide variety of commercial situations, for a wide variety of types of work and in any location.

- It is a clear and simple document – using language and a structure which are straightforward and easily understood.

NEC Professional Services Contract is one of the NEC family and is consistent with all other NEC3 documents. This document comprises the Guidance Notes and Flow Charts for the NEC Professional Services Contract.

ISBN (complete box set) 0 7277 3382 6
ISBN (Professional Services Contract) 0 7277 3370 2
ISBN (this document) 0 7277 3371 0

First edition 1994
Second edition 1998
Third edition June 2005

Cover photo, Golden Jubilee Bridge, courtesy of City of Westminster

9 8 7 6 5 4 3 2 1

British Library Cataloguing in Publication Data for this publication is available from the British Library.

Typeset by Academic + Technical, Bristol

Printed and bound in Great Britain by Bell & Bain Limited, Glasgow, UK

CONTENTS

ACKNOWLEDGEMENTS

The first edition of the NEC Professional Services Contract was drafted by Peter Higgins working on behalf of the Institution of Civil Engineers, with the assistance of Frank Griffiths of the Chartered Institute of Purchasing and Supply and Michael Coleman of the Association of Project Managers. Dr Martin Barnes then of Coopers and Lybrand advised on the co-ordination of the contract with the NEC.

For the second edition of the NEC Professional Services Contract the guidance notes were produced by the Institution of Civil Engineers through its NEC Panel and were mainly drafted by Bill Weddell and Tom Nicholson, with the assistance of Peter Higgins, as members of the NEC Panel. The flow charts were produced by John Perry, Ross Hayes and colleagues at the University of Birmingham.

For the third edition of the NEC Professional Services Contract these Guidance Notes were produced by the Institution of Civil Engineers and were mainly drafted by Bill Weddell with the assistance of members of the NEC Panel. The Flow Charts were produced by Robert Gerrard with assistance from Ross Hayes and Tom Nicholson.

The original NEC was designed and drafted by Dr Martin Barnes then of Coopers and Lybrand with the assistance of Professor J. G. Perry then of the University of Birmingham, T. W. Weddell then of Travers Morgan Management, T. H. Nicholson, Consultant to the Institution of Civil Engineers, A. Norman then of the University of Manchester Institute of Science and Technology and P. A. Baird, then Corporate Contracts Consultant, Eskom, South Africa.

The members of the NEC Panel are:

P. Higgins, BSc, CEng, FICE, FCIArb (Chairman)
P. A. Baird, BSc, CEng, FICE, M(SA)ICE, MAPM
M. Barnes, BSc(Eng), PhD, FREng, FICE, FCIOB, CCMI, ACIArb, MBCS, FInstCES, FAPM
A. J. Bates, FRICS, MInstCES
A. J. M. Blackler, BA, LLB(Cantab), MCIArb
P. T. Cousins, BEng(Tech), DipArb, CEng, MICE, MCIArb, MCMI
L. T. Eames, BSc, FRICS, FCIOB
F. Forward, BA(Hons), DipArch, MSc(Const Law), RIBA, FCIArb
Professor J. G. Perry, MEng, PhD, CEng, FICE, MAPM
N. C. Shaw, FCIPS, CEng, MIMechE
T. W. Weddell, BSc, CEng, DIC, FICE, FIStructE, ACIArb

NEC Consultant:

R. A. Gerrard, BSc(Hons), MRICS, FCIArb, FInstCES

Secretariat:

A. Cole, LLB, LLM, BL
J. M. Hawkins, BA(Hons), MSc
F. N. Vernon (Technical Adviser), BSc, CEng, MICE

FOREWORD

The first edition of the Professional Services Contract (PSC) was published in 1994 as part of the New Engineering Contract (NEC) family of contracts. It was designed for the purpose of appointing professionals to carry out various roles in the NEC contracts (*Project Manager*, *Supervisor*, designers) and for the wider use of appointing professionals where the NEC was not used, or even when no construction work was required.

As Employers have begun to appreciate the benefits of the PSC and the NEC principles on which it has been drafted, they are using it in many different circumstances. Its structure permits wide flexibility in the choice of different options of payment to the Consultant, as well as in the allocation of risk between the Parties. Its incorporation of established management procedures has also been seen to be of considerable benefit.

With the increasing use of partnering arrangements, Employers have sought conditions of contract which are compatible with partnering. For the appointment of professionals, the PSC with its non-adversarial approach, has been seen to be well suited for this purpose. It is also anticipated that wider use of the PSC will be made by local authorities in appointing individuals and firms to provide professional services previously done in-house.

As a result of experience in using the PSC, and changes in the construction industry in the wake of the Latham Report, published in 1994, it became evident that various amendments were required and that several improvements to the PSC could be made. Accordingly the second edition was produced under the supervision of the NEC Panel. Flow charts which were used to check the drafting of clauses were also included. The Panel also had the benefit of comments of the Construction Industry Council's Task Force, which was established to investigate harmonisation of conditions of engagement (1994–5).

As in the first edition, the method of resolving disputes is adjudication. Since publication of the first edition, the UK Parliament has provided a right to adjudication for any disputing party in construction contracts (including professional services agreements) in the form of the UK Housing Grants, Construction and Regeneration Act 1996. Since the PSC, like all other standard forms of contract, does not comply with the Act, a secondary Option Y(UK)2 and Option W2 have been included for use where the Act applies to UK contracts.

The third edition of the Professional Services Contract has been produced to incorporate suggestions made by users of the second edition, and also other changes which reflect recent developments in the construction industry.

nec3 Guidance Notes for the Professional Services Contract

INTRODUCTION

The NEC Professional Services Contract (PSC) has been developed as part of the New Engineering Contract (NEC) system of contract documents. The PSC has been drafted with the same objectives as the NEC and has adopted clauses from the NEC Engineering and Construction Contract (ECC) where they were considered to be appropriate for the appointment of a professional organisation or person.

The purpose of the document is to form a standard contract for the appointment of consultants providing professional services to be used in engineering and construction generally. It can be used for the appointment of a project manager or a supervisor under an NEC contract and also for the appointment of persons fulfilling other roles associated with construction contracts (such as a designer responsible either directly to the Employer or to the Contractor in a construction contract) or for appointments of consultants in advance of construction (e.g. appointment of a project manager or designer during the early development stages of a project).

Its use however is not limited to projects where other NEC contracts are being used. It can be used where no construction works are to take place or where other forms of contract for construction are being used. When the PSC is used by a contractor (for instance, to appoint a designer as a subcontractor in a 'design and construct' contract) the contractor has the role of 'Employer' in the PSC. In such circumstances, the PSC can be used as a subcontract (ECC clause 26) with appropriate amendments. (See Appendices 3 and 4.)

The contract has been drafted as a 'shell' contract which requires important information to be provided separately. The most critical document to be provided is the Scope. This contains the detailed requirements of the *Employer* and is frequently referred to within the PSC.

The purpose of these guidance notes is to explain the reasons for some of the provisions in the PSC and to provide guidance on how to use it. Where clauses are similar to those in the ECC, reference may be made to the ECC guidance notes for further explanation. The flow charts show the procedural logic on which the PSC is based and are published in this volume for reference.

The NEC conventions of using italics for terms which are identified in the Contract Data and capital initials for terms defined in the PSC have been used in these guidance notes. Neither the guidance notes nor the flow charts are contract documents, nor are they part of the PSC. They should not be used for legal interpretation of the meaning of the PSC.

CONTRACT STRATEGY

The *Employer* chooses the contract strategy. This determines the specific professional *services* to be carried out, the basis of payment and the balance of risks between *Employer* and *Consultant*. The decision on contract strategy will identify the options from the Professional Services Contract to be chosen, the need for other provisions, and some of the material to appear in the Scope.

The main Options

There are four types of payment mechanism available through the main Options.

Option A	Priced contract with activity schedule
Option C	Target contract
Option E	Time based contract
Option G	Term contract

For a particular contract, one main Option must be chosen. The clauses from the selected main Option are combined with the core clauses, the appropriate dispute resolution Option (W1 or W2), and the clauses from the selected secondary Options to provide a complete contract.

The main Options provide different allocations of risk between the *Employer* and the *Consultant* and use different arrangements for payment to the *Consultant*.

- Option A is a lump sum priced contract in which the risks of being able to Provide the Services at the agreed prices in the *activity schedule* are largely borne by the *Consultant*.
- Option C is a target contract in which the financial risks are shared by the *Employer* and the *Consultant* in agreed proportions.
- Option E is a type of cost reimbursable contract in which the financial risk is largely borne by the *Employer*.
- Option G is a term contract in which various items of work are priced or stated to be on a time basis. Thus the risk of being able to perform the instructed Tasks at the agreed prices or *staff rates* is largely borne by the *Consultant*, whilst the *Employer* retains control over the individual Tasks to be carried out.

The *ad valorem* or percentage fee type of contract has not been included as an option. Under this arrangement, payments to the *Consultant* are an agreed percentage of the works construction cost. This implies that the cost of the *Consultant's* services is proportional to the cost of constructing the works. Its merits were carefully considered, but rejected for the following reasons.

- The *Consultant* has no incentive to produce an economical design or other service.
- The cost of construction is largely a function of the market and bears no relation to the cost of professional services.
- The final cost of construction (and therefore the final fee) is not established until after construction is complete, whilst most professional costs are expended much earlier and even before construction starts.
- The effect of variations to the Scope on the payments due to the *Consultant* are difficult to assess.

Option A: Priced contract with activity schedule

Under this contract the *Consultant* is paid a lump sum for the *services*. An *activity schedule* is a list of the activities which the *Consultant* expects to carry out in Providing the Services. When it has been prepared and priced by the *Consultant*, the lump sum for each activity is the price to be paid by the *Employer* for that activity. The total of these prices is the *Consultant's* lump sum price for providing the whole of the *services*.

Option C: Target contract

Target contracts are sometimes used where the extent of work to be done is not fully defined or where anticipated risks are greater. Although used frequently in construction contracts, they have had limited application in consultancy contracts. The financial risk is shared between the *Consultant* and the *Employer* in the following way.

- The *Consultant* tenders a target price in the form of a priced *activity schedule*. The target price is the *Consultant*'s estimate of Providing the Services and is defined as the total of the Prices.
- The *Consultant* tenders his *staff rates*.
- During the course of the contract the *Consultant* is paid the Time Charge, which is the staff time for the *services* carried out priced at the appropriate *staff rates*. This is defined as the Price for Services Provided to Date
- At the end of the contract, if the final Price for Services Provided to Date is less than the final total of the Prices, the *Consultant* is paid his share of the difference according to the formula stated in the Contract Data. If the final Price for Services Provided to Date is greater than the final total of the Prices, the *Consultant* pays his share of the difference.

The Scope must be sufficiently descriptive to enable the *Consultant* to price the *services* in his tender.

The target price set at the Contract Date may change during the contract as the compensation events procedure is applied to changes in the Scope and other compensation events.

Option E: Time based contract

This is a cost reimbursable type of contract which should be used when the *services* cannot be defined sufficiently accurately for a lump sum to be quoted. In such circumstances the *Consultant* cannot be expected to take cost risks other than those which the control of his employees and other resources entails. He carries minimum risk and is paid the Time Charge (as defined by the *staff rates* stated in the contract).

Option G: Term contract

This contract provides for the appointment of a *Consultant* for a term (an agreed period of time). The *Consultant* prices a *task schedule* prepared in advance by the *Employer* as well as providing *staff rates* for different grades of staff. Each price on the *task schedule* is a lump sum for that particular item. Some items on the *task schedule* may be stated to be carried out on a time basis rather than for a lump sum price.

When the *Employer* requires specific services to be carried out by the *Consultant* he identifies a proposed Task by selecting individual items from the *task schedule*. Any items not on the *task schedule* are notified as compensation events and the compensation event assessment procedure is used to determine how each item is to be paid for. The *Consultant* carries out each Task only when he has been instructed to do so by the *Employer*.

Dispute resolution Options

There are two procedures included for the resolution of disputes.

- Option W1
- Option W2

One of these must be selected and the choice depends on whether the UK Housing Grants, Construction and Regeneration Act 1996 applies to the contract. Under this Act, a construction contract includes 'an agreement –

a. to do architectural, design or surveying work, or
b. to provide advice on building, engineering, interior or exterior decoration or on the laying-out of landscape,

in relation to construction operations'.

Thus, many contracts in the United Kingdom for providing professional services are subject to the Act. Option W2 has been drafted as a dispute resolution procedure which complies with the Act. Option W1 should be selected for all non-UK contracts and contracts which are not construction contracts as defined in the Act. The selection of Option W1 or Option W2 should be indicated in part one of the Contract Data.

Dispute resolution Option W1

This Option should be selected whenever the United Kingdom Housing Grants, Construction and Regeneration Act 1996 does not apply to the contract in question.

It is the intention that disputes should be referred to and resolved by the *Adjudicator*. If either Party is dissatisfied with the *Adjudicator*'s decision and wishes to pursue the matter further, he is free to refer it to arbitration or the courts, whichever is identified as the *tribunal* in the Contract Data. The Parties may deal with the dispute by other means if they agree to do so. The key periods affecting dispute procedures are illustrated in Figures 1, 2 and 3 which should be referred to in conjunction with the notes.

Dispute resolution W1

W1.1 Disputes are to be dealt with by adjudication in the first instance.

The *Adjudicator* W1.2
(1) The person appointed as *Adjudicator* is named in part one of the Contract Data. He is to be appointed jointly by the Parties using the NEC Adjudicator's Contract (one of the documents of the NEC family of standard contracts). His fees and expenses are shared equally between the Parties to a dispute, regardless of his decision, unless otherwise agreed.

The *Adjudicator* should be a person with experience of the kind of services required of the *Consultant* and who occupies or has occupied a senior position dealing with similar dispute problems. He should be able to understand the point of view of both *Employer* and *Consultant*, to judge the required level of skill and care and be able to act impartially.

(2) The obligation of impartiality is fundamental to the role of the *Adjudicator*. The duty is repeated in the NEC Adjudicator's Contract. The *Adjudicator*'s status is different from that of an arbitrator.

(3) The *Adjudicator* is appointed jointly by the *Employer* and the *Consultant* for the contract. The *Employer* should insert his choice of *Adjudicator* in part one of the Contract Data. If the *Consultant* does not agree with the choice, a suitable person will be the subject of discussion and agreement before the Contract Date. Alternatively, the *Employer* may propose a list of acceptable names, and the *Consultant* may be asked to select one of them to be *Adjudicator*. Some *Employers* may prefer *Consultants* to propose suitable names.

Where an *Adjudicator* has not been named in the Contract Data, this subclause describes the procedure for appointing one. The procedure also applies where a replacement adjudicator is needed in the event that the named *Adjudicator* has resigned or is unable to act. In the UK there are several *Adjudicator nominating bodies* who are able to appoint a suitable person to act as *Adjudicator*.

(4) Any existing disputes on which the original *Adjudicator* has not made a decision are automatically referred to the replacement adjudicator. It is important that the Parties ensure that the replacement adjudicator receives all the relevant information. The time stated in the contract for supply of information then runs from the time of appointment of the replacement adjudicator.

If a need arises for a temporary replacement adjudicator (e.g. during the *Adjudicator*'s holiday), the Parties should agree a temporary appointment.

Consultant becomes aware of action or lack of action of *Employer*

Four weeks maximum

Consultant notifies *Employer* of dispute

Two weeks minimum
Four weeks maximum (or greater agreed period)

Consultant refers dispute to *Adjudicator* and includes information

Four weeks (or greater agreed period) maximum

Parties may provide *Adjudicator* with further information

Four weeks (or greater agreed period) maximum

Adjudicator notifies Parties of decision with reasons

Four weeks maximum

A Party may notify the other Party of intention to refer dispute to *tribunal*

Tribunal starts proceedings and settles dispute

Figure 1. Steps in adjudication under Option W1 for a disputed action or lack of action on the part of the *Employer*.

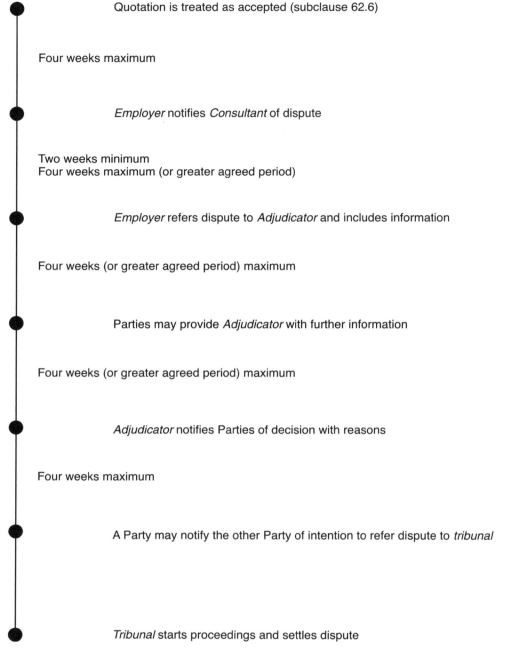

Quotation is treated as accepted (subclause 62.6)

Four weeks maximum

Employer notifies *Consultant* of dispute

Two weeks minimum
Four weeks maximum (or greater agreed period)

Employer refers dispute to *Adjudicator* and includes information

Four weeks (or greater agreed period) maximum

Parties may provide *Adjudicator* with further information

Four weeks (or greater agreed period) maximum

Adjudicator notifies Parties of decision with reasons

Four weeks maximum

A Party may notify the other Party of intention to refer dispute to *tribunal*

Tribunal starts proceedings and settles dispute

Figure 2. Steps in adjudication under Option W1 for a disputed about a quotation for a compensation event which is treated as having been accepted.

Either Party notifies other Party of disputed matter

Two weeks minimum
Four weeks maximum (or greater agreed period)

Either Party refers dispute to *Adjudicator* and includes information

Four weeks (or greater agreed period) maximum

Parties may provide *Adjudicator* with further information

Four weeks (or greater agreed period) maximum

Adjudicator notifies Parties of decision with reasons

Four weeks maximum

Tribunal starts proceedings and settles dispute

Figure 3. Steps in adjudication under Option W1 for any other disputed matter.

	(5)	It is important that the person appointed as *Adjudicator* is protected from legal actions by the Parties and others.
The adjudication	W1.3 (1)	This subclause requires that any of the four categories of dispute listed in the Adjudication Table is referred to the *Adjudicator*. Time limits are provided for notification of the dispute to the other Party and for reference to the *Adjudicator*. The procedures for the four categories of dispute are shown diagrammatically in Figures 1, 2 and 3.
	(2)	The Parties are barred from referring a dispute to the *Adjudicator* or the *tribunal* outside the stated time limits.
	(3)	It is important that the *Adjudicator* has all the relevant information to enable him to reach a decision. The Parties are required to submit all information supporting their case within four weeks of the referral to the *Adjudicator*, or greater agreed period.
	(4a)	Where a dispute which affects services being carried out by a Subconsultant arises and which may constitute a dispute between the *Consultant* and Subconsultant as well as between the *Consultant* and the *Employer*, there is provision for the matter to be resolved between the three Parties by the *Adjudicator* named in this contract. This prevents the dispute being dealt with by different adjudicators who may make different decisions. This does mean, however, that the adjudicator named in the subcontract will not be used for the dispute under that subcontract, and the Subconsultant will be obliged to use an *Adjudicator* he has not previously agreed to. It would be helpful if the *Adjudicator*'s name is included in the subconsultancy contract documents so that Subconsultants have prior knowledge of the identity of the *Adjudicator* in the main contract.
	(4b)	This subclause applies only when the PSC is used as a subcontract. (See also Appendices 3 and 4.)
	(5)	Although the *Adjudicator* is empowered to review and revise any action or inaction of the *Employer* and alter a quotation treated as having been accepted, the Parties are not permitted to widen the dispute to include other disputes which might have occurred after the original submission. The *Adjudicator* has wide powers under this subclause. He may seek information himself in addition to information submitted by the Parties.
	(6)	It is important that copies of the communications sent to the *Adjudicator* are sent to the other Party so that each Party is aware of the other Party's case.
	(7),(8) &(9)	The *Adjudicator* in notifying his decision is required to state reasons for his decision and also to include his assessment of additional cost and delay as appropriate. Pending settlement of the dispute, the Parties proceed with their duties under the contract.
		In complex disputes and for other valid reasons the *Adjudicator* may require a period greater than the four weeks stated. An extension of the period requires the agreement of the Parties. If such agreement is not forthcoming and the *Adjudicator* cannot or for some other reason does not notify his decision within the four week period, either Party may refer the dispute to the *tribunal* under subclause W1.4(3).
	(10)	A valid decision by the *Adjudicator* is enforceable in the courts. The decision is also final unless within four weeks the dissatisfied Party has notified his intention to refer the dispute to the *tribunal* (subclause W1.4(2)).
Review by the *tribunal*	W1.4 (1)	Initially the *Employer*, and by acceptance also the *Consultant* and Subconsultant, will select the method of final and binding dispute resolution. It can be either arbitration or litigation in the appropriate court.
		If arbitration is chosen, the entry in the Contract Data against the *tribunal* is 'arbitration' together with the *arbitration procedure* and other details proposed for the conduct of the arbitration (subclause W1.4(5)).

If litigation is chosen, appropriate entries must be made for the jurisdiction chosen. In England and Wales, the *tribunal* might be 'trial by a judge sitting as such in the High Court of Justice in London'. Advice should be taken, however, on the appropriate entry to provide for the jurisdiction intended.

(2) A dispute cannot be referred to arbitration or litigation unless it has been referred to the *Adjudicator*. A time limit is given for notification of intention to refer the matter to the *tribunal*, after which the *Adjudicator*'s decision will be final and no further notification of intended reference to the *tribunal* may be made. If the adjudication involves three Parties – i.e. a subconsultant is joined in the adjudication – the dispute resolution by the *tribunal* will also involve all three parties.

(3) A dispute may be referred to the *tribunal* where the *Adjudicator* has failed to notify his decision in time, as well as where a dissatisfied Party wishes to take the matter further.

Dispute resolution Option W2

This Option should be selected whenever the United Kingdom Housing Grants, Construction and Regeneration Act 1996 (the Act) applies to the contract in question.

It is the intention that disputes should be referred to and resolved by the *Adjudicator.* If either Party is dissatisfied with the *Adjudicator*'s decision and wishes to pursue the matter further, he is free to refer it to arbitration or the courts, whichever is identified as the *tribunal* in the Contract Data. The Parties may deal with the dispute by other means if they agree to do so. The key periods affecting dispute procedures are illustrated in Figure 4 which should be referred to in conjunction with these notes.

Dispute resolution

W2

W2.1
(1) Disputes are to be dealt with by adjudication in the first instance. The phrase 'at any time' is a requirement of the Act. The only limit to this time is the limitation period for the contract. This means that disputes arising several years after the *Consultant* has completed his work may be submitted to the *Adjudicator.*

(2) Generally time periods in the PSC are stated in weeks. In Option W2 and the Act, time periods are in days, which means that 'day' must be defined. The definition in this subclause is as in the Act. Days include Saturdays and Sundays.

The *Adjudicator*

W2.2
(1) The person appointed as *Adjudicator* is named in part one of the Contract Data. He is to be appointed jointly by the Parties using the NEC Adjudicator's Contract (one of the NEC family of standard contracts). His fees are shared equally between the Parties to a dispute, regardless of his decision, unless otherwise agreed.

The A*djudicator* should be a person with experience of the kind of *services* required of the *Consultant* and who occupies or has occupied a senior position dealing with similar dispute problems. He should be able to understand the point of view of both *Employer* and *Consultant,* to judge the required level of competence and be able to act impartially.

(2) The obligation of impartiality is fundamental to the role of *Adjudicator.* The duty is repeated in the NEC Adjudicator's Contract. The *Adjudicator*'s status is different from that of an arbitrator.

(3) The *Adjudicator* is appointed jointly by the *Employer* and the *Consultant* for the contract. The *Employer* should insert his choice of *Adjudicator* in part one of the Contract Data. If the *Consultant* does not agree with the choice, a suitable person will be the subject of discussion and agreement before the Contract Date. Alternatively, the *Employer* may propose a list of acceptable names and the *Consultant* may be asked to select one of them to be *Adjudicator*. Some *Employer*s may prefer *Consultant*s to propose suitable names.

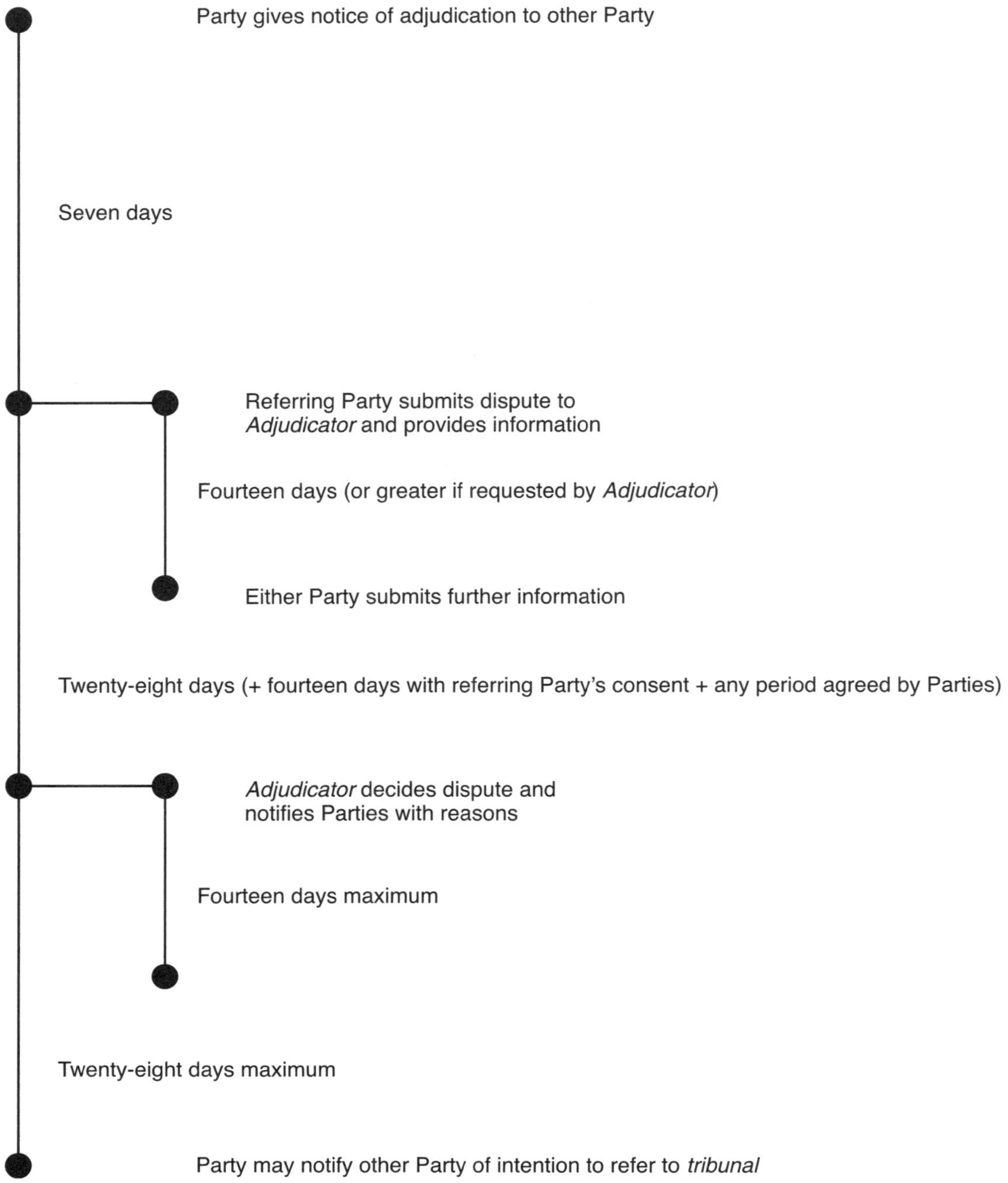

Party gives notice of adjudication to other Party

Seven days

Referring Party submits dispute to
Adjudicator and provides information

Fourteen days (or greater if requested by *Adjudicator*)

Either Party submits further information

Twenty-eight days (+ fourteen days with referring Party's consent + any period agreed by Parties)

Adjudicator decides dispute and
notifies Parties with reasons

Fourteen days maximum

Twenty-eight days maximum

Party may notify other Party of intention to refer to *tribunal*

Figure 4. Steps in adjudication under Option W2

Where an *Adjudicator* has not been named in the Contract Data, this subclause describes the procedure for appointing one. The procedure also applies where a replacement adjudicator is needed in the event that the named *Adjudicator* is unable to act. In the UK there are several *Adjudicator nominating bodies* who are able to appoint a suitable person as *Adjudicator.*

(4)   Any existing disputes on which the original *Adjudicator* has not made a decision are automatically referred to the replacement adjudicator. It is important that the Parties ensure that the replacement adjudicator receives all relevant information. The time stated in the contract for supply of information then runs from the time of appointment of the replacement adjudicator. If a need arises for a temporary replacement adjudicator, e.g. during the *Adjudicator*'s holiday, the Parties should agree a temporary appointment.

(5)   It is important that the person appointed as *Adjudicator* is protected from legal actions by the Parties and others. It is also a requirement of the Act.

The adjudication   W2.3   The Party wishing to refer the dispute for adjudication initiates the procedure
(1)   by giving a notice to the other Party, with a copy to the *Adjudicator.* The procedure also confirms or otherwise whether the *Adjudicator* is to proceed with the adjudication.

The time periods in this subclause and subclause W2.2(3) are designed to ensure that an adjudicator is appointed within seven days as required by the Act.

(2)   It is important that the *Adjudicator* has all the relevant information to enable him to reach his decision. The Parties are required to submit all information supporting their case within fourteen days of the referral of the dispute to the *Adjudicator* or greater agreed period.

(3a)   Where a dispute which affects services being carried out by a Subconsultant arises and which may constitute a dispute between the *Consultant* and the Subconsultant as well as between the *Consultant* and the *Employer*, there is provision for the matter to be resolved between the three Parties by the *Adjudicator* named in this contract. This prevents the dispute being dealt with by different adjudicators who may make different decisions. This does mean however that the adjudicator named in the subcontract will not be used for the dispute under that subcontract, and the Subconsultant will be obliged to use an *Adjudicator* he has not previously agreed to. It would be helpful if the *Adjudicator*'s name is included in the subconsultancy contract documents so that Subconsultants have prior knowledge of the identity of the *Adjudicator* in the main contract.

Because of the timing requirements of the Act, this process will only be practical with the agreement of the Subconsultant.

(3b)   This subclause applies only where the PSC is used as a subcontract. (See also Appendices 3 and 4.)

(4)   Although the *Adjudicator* is empowered to review and revise any action or inaction of the *Employer* and alter a quotation treated as having been accepted, the Parties are not permitted unless agreed by the Parties and the *Adjudicator* to widen the dispute to include other disputes which might have occurred after the original submission. The *Adjudicator* has wide powers under this subclause. He may seek information himself in addition to information submitted by the Parties.

(5)   It is important that any delay caused by a Party does not delay or stop the adjudication. Thus, where a Party does not comply with the *Adjudicator*'s instructions, the adjudication continues. This would also apply where a Party refuses to take part in the adjudication.

(6)   It is important that copies of the communications sent to the *Adjudicator* are sent to the other Party so that each Party is aware of the other Party's case.

(8) The *Adjudicator* in notifying his decision is required to state reasons for his decision and also to include his assessment of additional cost and delay as appropriate.

In complex disputes and for other valid reasons the *Adjudicator* may require a period greater than the twenty-eight days stated. An extension of fourteen days may be granted if the referring Party agrees, or other period if both Parties agree.

(11) A valid decision by the *Adjudicator* is enforceable in the courts. The decision is also final unless within four weeks the dissatisfied Party has notified his intention to refer the dispute to the *tribunal* under subclause W2.4(2).

Review by the *tribunal* W2.4 (1) The *Employer* should insert in the Contact Data the *tribunal* that will decide a dispute if either Party does not accept the *Adjudicator*'s decision. The choice will normally be either arbitration or the courts. An individual person should not be named.

(3) The *tribunal* has wide powers to settle the dispute and is not tied to a decision or action of the *Employer*. Referral of a dispute to the *tribunal* should not be regarded as an appeal against the *Adjudicator*'s decision. Thus, the Parties may rely on new evidence and submissions that were not put before the *Adjudicator*.

(4) Standard arbitration procedures generally deal with appointment of arbitrators, replacement arbitrators and time limits. Standard procedures for civil engineering works in the UK include those published by the Institution of Civil Engineers, and for building works those published by the Joint Contracts Tribunal (JCT).

The secondary Options After deciding the main Option and the appropriate dispute resolution Option, the *Employer* may choose any of the secondary Options.

Option X1	Price adjustment for inflation
Option X2	Changes in the law
Option X3	Multiple currencies (used only with Options A and G)
Option X4	Parent company guarantee
Option X5	Sectional Completion (not used with Option G)
Option X6	Bonus for early Completion (not used with Option G)
Option X7	Delay damages
Option X8	*Collateral warranty agreements*
Option X9	Transfer of rights
Option X10	*Employer's Agent*
Option X11	Termination by the *Employer*
Option X12	Partnering
Option X13	Performance bond
Option X18	Limitation of liability
Option X20	Key Performance Indicators (not used with Option X12)
Option Y(UK)2	The Housing Grants, Construction and Regeneration Act 1996
Option Y(UK)3	The Contracts (Rights of Third Parties) Act 1999
Option Z	*Additional conditions of contract*

Any combination of secondary Options may be used.

Option X1: Price adjustment for inflation

This Option should be used if the *Employer* decides to accept the risk of inflation.

The price adjustment factor (PAF) is calculated on each anniversary of the Contract Date (subclause X1.1) and is then used during the following year to make adjustments for inflation.

The *Employer* decides which published *index* to use, e.g. the Retail Prices Index, and enters this in part one of the Contract Data.

The *Consultant's staff rates* stated in part two of the Contract Data may be either

- fixed, and thus not variable with changes in salary actually paid to individuals or
- variable with changes in salary paid to individuals.

Fixed *staff rates*

In all the main Options, a price adjustment factor is calculated as stated in subclause X1.1. This factor is used for calculating the additional amount due and adjustment of *expenses* in all main Options.

For target contracts (Option C), an amount for price adjustment is added to the Prices (subclause X1.3) so that the total of the Prices can be fairly compared with the final Price for Services Provided to Date (the Time Charge using variable *staff rates*) for calculating the *Consultant's* share.

Variable *staff rates*

Different subclauses are used according to which main Option applies, as follows.

Option A	Subclauses X1.1	X1.2	X1.5	X1.6
Option C	Subclauses X1.1	X1.3	X1.5	X1.6
Option E	Subclauses X1.1	X1.6		
Option G	Subclauses X1.1	X1.4	X1.5	X1.6

For a priced contract using an *activity schedule* (Option A), an amount for price adjustment is calculated as stated in subclauses X1.1 and X1.2. The Time Charge to be used in the assessment of compensation events is adjusted to the Contract Date using subclause X1.5 in order to maintain the time basis of the Prices.

For target contracts (Option C), an amount for price adjustment is added to the Prices (subclause X1.3) so that the total of the Prices can be fairly compared with the final Price for Services Provided to Date (the Time Charge using variable *staff rates*) for calculating the *Consultant's* share. The Time Charge to be used in the assessment of compensation events is adjusted to the Contract Date using subclause X1.5.

For term contracts (Option G), a price adjustment is necessary only for the lump sum items in the *task schedule* using subclause X1.4. The Time Charge to be used in the assessment of compensation events (for the lump sum items added to the *task schedule* under subclause 55.1) is adjusted to the Contract Date using subclause X1.5.

Expenses

For all the main Options (Options A, C, E and G), if the *expenses* are stated in the Contract Data as fixed prices and are not adjustable for inflation, an amount for *expenses* adjustment should be included in the amount due in accordance with subclause X1.6.

Worked examples of the calculations of the amounts for price adjustment and *expenses* adjustment are given in Table 1.

Option X2: Changes in the law   X2.1

This Option reduces the effect on the *Consultant's* costs and programme of the risk of changes to the *law of the project* which occurs after the Contract Date by making such a change a compensation event. Such changes can have a dramatic effect on the *Consultant's* costs and his liability to make progress on the *services*.

nec 3 Guidance notes and flow charts for the Professional Services Contract

Table 1. Option X1: Price adjustment for inflation – worked examples

	Contract Date	1st anniversary	2nd anniversary
(I) Price adjustment			
Index } (subclause X1.1)	100	105	110
PAF }	0.0	0.05	0.10
(a) Fixed staff rates (Options A, C, E and G)			
Change in PSPD	NO PRICE ADJUSTMENT	£20,000	£20,000
Change in price adjustment amount (subclause X1.2)		£20,000 × 0.05 = £1,000	£20,000 × 0.10 = £2,000
(b) Variable staff rates			
Option A and Option G (lump sum items only)			
Change in PSPD	NO PRICE ADJUSTMENT	£20,000	£20,000
Change in price adjustment amount (Option A – subclause X1.2. Option G – subclause X1.4)		£20,000 × 0.05 = £1,000	£20,000 × 0.10 = £2,000
Staff rates for compensation event assessment (subclause X1.5)	NO ADJUSTMENT	Current staff rate ÷ 1.05	Current staff rate ÷ 1.10
Option C			
Change in PSPD	NO ADJUSTMENT	£20,000	£20,000
Addition to Prices (subclause X1.3)		£20,000 × 0.05 ÷ 1.05 = £952.38	£20,000 × 0.10 ÷ 1.10 = £1,818.18
Staff rates for compensation event assessment (subclause X1.5)	NO ADJUSTMENT	Current staff rate ÷ 1.05	Current staff rate ÷ 1.10
(ii) Fixed expenses adjustment			
Options A, C, E and G			
Change in fixed expenses	NO EXPENSES ADJUSTMENT	£2,000	£2,000
Change in expenses adjustment amount (subclause X1.6)		£2,000 × 0.05 = £100	£2,000 × 0.10 = £200

The *Employer* should review the laws which could be relevant to the *services* and identify those where he is prepared to carry the risk of changes as *law of the project* in the Contract Data. These could be the *law of the contract* (subclause 12.2), or the law of the country where the services are to be provided, where the construction site is or where a major supplier is located.

For the purposes of this subclause, the law includes a national or state statute, ordinance, decree, regulation (including building or safety regulations), by-law of a local or other duly constituted authority and other delegated legislation.

The subclause is reciprocal in the sense that it may result in either increased or reduced payment to the *Consultant*.

Option X3: Multiple currencies (used only with Options A and G)	X3.1	This Option is used (in conjunction with main Options A and G only) when it is intended that payment to the *Consultant* should be made in more than one currency and that the risk of changes in the *exchange rates* should be carried by the *Employer*.

The *Employer* should state in the Contract Data which items and activities are to be paid for in currencies other than the *currency of this contract*, what those currencies are, the maximum amounts payable in each currency and the *exchange rates* to be used in calculating the payments. *Exchange rates* are usually those published some two weeks before the *Consultant* submits his offer to the *Employer*. Any subsequent movement of the *exchange rates* is therefore at the *Employer*'s risk. No provision is made for multiple currencies in main Options C and E because the *Consultant* is paid the Time Charge.

Option X4: Parent company guarantee	X4.1	This Option should be included where the *Employer* requires the greater security provided by the parent company for the performance of the *Consultant*. The parent company guarantee should be provided by the Contract Date. If that is not achieved, a four week limit is provided as a fall-back. The form of guarantee should be included in the Scope in part one of the Contract Data.

Option X5: Sectional Completion (not used with Option G)	X5.1	This Option should be included when the *Employer* requires parts of the *services* to be completed before the whole of the *services*. The parts are called *sections*, each of which should be identified in the Contract Data part one, with a *completion date* for each. Completion of the *sections* is followed by Completion of the whole of the *services*. The *sections* do not make up the whole of the *services*. Delay damages and bonus for early completion can be related to *section completion dates* by using Options X7 and X6 respectively.

Option X6: Bonus for early Completion (not used with Option G)	X6.1	Where Completion as early as possible would benefit the *Employer*, whether of all or a *section* of the *services*, the *Employer* can use this Option to achieve early Completion. The bonus calculated in accordance with this subclause will be included in the assessment occurring at Completion of the whole (or *section*) of the *services*.

Option X7: Delay damages	X7.1	Delay damages are the liquidated damages paid by the *Consultant* when he fails to complete the *services* (or *sections* of the *services* if Option X5 is also used) by the Completion Date. Under English law and some other legal systems, if it is not included, delay damages are 'at large' and the remedy open to the *Employer* is to bring an action for damages for the *Consultant*'s breach of contract. In this event, evidence of the actual damage suffered by the *Employer* is required.

The amount of delay damages should not exceed a genuine pre-estimate of the damage which will be suffered as a result of the *Consultant*'s breach. They are described as delay damages because these are not the only liquidated damages in the PSC. Interest on late payments as provided for in subclause 51.4 is a form of liquidated damages.

Appropriate entries for delay damages should be made in the Contract Data. They may represent cost to the *Employer* caused by delayed start to another contract, or simply interest on the capital invested in the *services* of which the *Employer* has been deprived of the benefit. Damages greater than a genuine pre-estimate constitute a penalty and are not generally enforceable under English law.

Since delay damages are amounts to be paid by the *Consultant*, appropriate deductions are made in the first assessment of the amount due, occurring after the Completion Date, and in subsequent assessments up to Completion.

X7.2   This subclause protects the *Consultant* when he has paid delay damages and a later assessment of compensation events results in a delay to the Completion Date. This could arise when a compensation event occurs at a late stage or if an *Adjudicator* or *tribunal* changes the assessment of a compensation event and the decision is made after delay damages have been paid.

Option X8: *Collateral warranty agreements*   X8.1   A *collateral warranty agreement* is an agreement entered into by the *Consultant* with purchasers or tenants or funding organisations (who are not the *Employer*) of an industrial or commercial development. It has the effect of binding the *Consultant* in contract, and creating legal liability toward parties other than the *Employer* which may not otherwise exist. Details of the *collateral warranty agreements* which the *Consultant* will be required to enter into should be stated in the Contract Data.

These details should include

- form of warranty agreement,
- limitation period,
- insurance requirements,
- rights of assignment, including number of assignments to subsequent purchasers/tenants, permitted and
- others providing warranty agreements.

A requirement to enter into such agreements can represent a considerable extension of a *Consultant*'s liability. Legal advice may be necessary and advisable. The British Property Federation has published model forms of collateral warranty which have been agreed by the ACE, RIAS, RIBA and RICS, after consultation with the Association of British Insurers.

Option Y(UK)3 also provides for third party rights for contracts in the UK.

Option X9: Transfer of rights   X9.1   The rights over drawings, documents, designs and the like prepared by the *Consultant* would normally remain with the *Consultant*. The core clauses recognise this but give the *Employer* entitlement to use any documents for the purposes stated in the Scope. If, in addition to this, the *Employer* wishes to obtain the rights for himself, this Option should be chosen.

Option X10: *Employer*'s Agent   X10.1   This Option should be used where a corporate body wishes to appoint an individual, either from within its own organisation or an external consultant, to act as its agent under this contract. The *Agent* should be identified and the extent of the *Agent*'s authority defined in the Contract Data.

Option X11: Termination by the *Employer*   X11.1   Under the core clauses the *Employer* is entitled to terminate following the substantial failure of the *Consultant* to carry out his obligations, on insolvency of the *Consultant* or when the *Employer* no longer requires the *services*. This Option gives a further power to the *Employer* to terminate the appointment of the *Consultant* for a reason not stated in the contract which might involve no default of the *Consultant*.

X11.2   This subclause gives the *Consultant* entitlement to increased payment if the *Employer* terminates for a reason not stated in the contract. The 5% payment is arbitrary, but recognises that the *Consultant* has been deprived of some profit which he would have made if he had been permitted to continue with, and complete, the *services*.

Option X12: Partnering

This Option is used for partnering between more than two parties working on the same project or projects or on the provision of services. The Option is included in all NEC contracts which each party has with the body which is paying for the work or service. The parties who have this Option included in their contracts are intended to make up the partnering team. Option X12, does not, however, create a multi-party contract.

The content of the Option is derived from the 'Guide to Project Team Partnering' published by the Construction Industry Council (CIC). The requirements of the CIC document that are not already in the NEC contracts are covered by this Option.

The purpose of the Option is to establish the NEC family as an effective contract basis for multi-party partnering. By linking this Option to other bi-party contracts, the NEC can be used

- for partnering for any number of projects and services,
- internationally,
- for projects and services of any technical composition and
- as far down the supply chain as required.

Parties must recognise that by entering into a contract which includes Option X12, they will be undertaking responsibilities additional to those in the basic NEC contract.

A dispute (or difference) between Partners who do not have a contract between themselves is resolved by the Core Group. This is the Group that manages the conduct of the Partners in accordance with the Partnering Information. If the Core Group is unable to resolve the issue, then it is resolved under the procedure of the Partners' individual contracts, either directly or indirectly with the *Client* who will always be involved at some stage in the contractual chain. The *Client* may seek to have issues on all contracts dealt with simultaneously.

Option X12 does not include direct remedies between non-contracting Partners to recover losses suffered by one of them caused by failure of the other. These remedies remain available in each Partner's individual contract, but their existence will encourage the parties to compromise any differences that arise. This applies to all levels of the supply chain, as a Consultant who is a Partner retains the responsibility for actions of a subconsultant who is a Partner. The final sanction against any Partner who fails to act as stated in Option X12 is for the Partner who employed them not to invite them to partner again.

There are many scenarios possible in which Option X12 may be used. The NEC family of contracts with Option X12 is sufficiently flexible to deal with them. For example, the contract may be an NEC Engineering and Construction Contract or an NEC Engineering and Construction Short Contract for a project. It may involve also an NEC Professional Services Contract. Later, an NEC Term Service Contract may cover maintenance of the asset created by the project and provision of other services for the *Client*.

Identified and defined terms

X12.1 (1) The point at which someone becomes a Partner is when his Own Contract (which includes Option X12) comes into existence. They should be named in the Schedule of Partners, and their representative identified.

(3) Not every Partner is a member of the Core Group.

(5) There are two options for subcontractor partners. Either the amount payable cascades down if the schedule allocates the same bonus/cost to the main contractor and subcontractor, or the main contractor absorbs the bonus/cost and does not pass it on.

Working together X12.3 The Core Group organises and holds meetings. It produces and distributes
(5) records of each meeting which includes agreed actions. Instructions from
the Core Group are issued in accordance with the Partner's Own Contract. The
Core Group may invite other Partners or people to attend a meeting of the
Core Group.

(8) The Partners should give advice and assistance when asked, and in addition
whenever they identify something that would be helpful to another Partner.

(9) A subcontractor may be a Partner, but the general policy on this should be
decided at the beginning of the project or service contract. The Core Group
should advise the Contractor at the outset if a subcontractor is to be asked to
be a Partner. A subcontractor who the Core Group decides should be a Partner
should not be appointed if he is unwilling to be a Partner.

Incentives X12.4 If one Partner lets the others down for a particular project or service by poor
(1) performance, then all lose their bonus for that target. If the *Employer* tries to
prevent a target being met, he is in breach of subclause 10.1.

There can be more than one Key Performance Indicator (KPI) for each partner.
KPIs may apply to one Partner, to several Partners or to all Partners.

Example of a KPI

KPI	Highways licensing of skips
Target	Skip applications decided within 3 days
Measurement	Number of applications decided
Amount	Main contractor £5 per application
	Subcontractor £30 per application

(2) The *Client* should consult with the other Partners before adding a KPI. The
effect on subcontracted work should be noted. Adding a KPI to work which is
subcontracted can involve a change to the KPI for a subcontractor.

Schedule of Partners

Date of last revision: . . . .

The Partners are the following.

Name of Partner	Representative's Address and contact details	Contribution and objective	Joining date	Leaving date	Key Performance Indicator	Target	Measurement arrangement	Amount of Payment if the target is improved upon or achieved*

* Enter *nil* in the last column if there is to be no money incentive

Schedule of Core Group Members

Date of last revision: . . . .

The Core Group members are the *Client* and the following.

Name of Partner	Address and contact details	Joining date	Leaving date

Option X13: Performance bond

X13.1 Where a performance bond is required by the *Employer* the ideal is that it should be provided by the Contract Date. If that is not achieved, a four week limit is provided as a fall-back. The form of the performance bond should be included in the Scope and the amount of the bond should be stated in the Contract Data.

Option X18: Limitation of liability

Limitation of liability

X18.1 & X18.2 Some situations under the PSC may involve risks of low probability but high impact. For this reason, it may be necessary for purely commercial reasons to limit the *Consultant*'s liability for certain risks. These subclauses state these limits, by reference to entries in the Contract Data.

X18.3 This subclause exempts the *Consultant* from any liability notified after the *end of liability date* which is stated in the Contract Data.

Option X20: Key Performance Indicators

X20.1 to X20.5 Key Performance Indicators (KPIs) are being increasingly used as a means of improving efficiency and encouraging better performance by *Consultant*s with a view to continuous improvement. KPIs are provided for in Option X12 where partnering arrangements are in place. This Option can be used to provide for KPIs when Option X12 is not used. The procedure in Option X20 requires the establishment of performance targets and regular reporting by the *Consultant* of his performance measured against the KPIs.

Option Y(UK)2: The Housing Grants, Construction and Regeneration Act 1996

This Option is prepared solely for use on contracts which are subject to the United Kingdom Housing Grants, Construction and Regeneration Act 1996 Part II (the Act). The Option should not be used in other circumstances.

The two principles contained in this Act which affect the NEC Professional Services Contract are those related to payment and adjudication. This Option deals only with the payment aspect. The adjudication aspect is dealt with under Option W2. The definition of a 'construction contract' in this Act is wide ranging and can be found in Section 104. It covers not only an agreement to carry out 'construction operations' but also 'an agreement to do architectural, design or surveying work, or to provide advice on building, engineering, interior or exterior decoration or on the laying-out of landscape in relation to construction operations'. Thus the Act will apply to many agreements made using the PSC.

The definition of a 'construction operation' can be found in Section 105(1) of the Act. The operations and contracts that are not subject to the Act are defined in Sections 105(2) and 106. In the United Kingdom (England, Wales, Scotland and Northern Ireland), the Parties to a contract should consider carefully whether the operation is subject to the Act before proceeding. If the operation or contract is subject to the Act, it is intended that, by incorporating Option Y(UK)2 into the contract, the payment provisions of the statutory Scheme for Construction Contracts do not become implied terms of the contract (Section 114(4)). Parties must be aware that it is not possible to contract out of a statutory requirement.

Subclause Y2.1 deals with the measurement of time periods in relation to the Act. Subclauses Y2.2 to 2.4 have been drafted with the intention of complying with Sections 109 to 113.

Y2.1 In the NEC family of contracts periods of time are usually measured in weeks thus avoiding complications of rest days and statutory holidays in different countries in which these contracts are used. The Act, however, defines most periods as a number of days. Section 116(3) of the Act states that Christmas Day, Good Friday and bank holidays are excluded from any period specified in the Act. Where the time period associated with the Act is referred to, that period has been stated in days in Option Y(UK)2.

The key periods affecting the procedure for payments when Option Y(UK)2 applies are illustrated in Figure 5, which includes references to the Act and to the Y(UK)2 subclauses. Figure 1 should be referred to in conjunction with the following notes on subclauses Y2.2 to Y2.4.

Y2.2
&
Y2.3
These additional clauses are drafted to accommodate Sections 109 to 111 of the Act. The *Employer* is now required to give notice to the *Consultant* of the payment to be made, and the basis on which the calculation is made. This is achieved by the third paragraph of subclause Y2.3.

Y2.3 augments core subclause 51.3 by requiring the *Employer* to notify the *Consultant* of any payment he intends to withold as required by Section 111 of the Act.

The Act uses very specific language about what and when 'payments become due' and when particular notices are issued and in defining the 'final date for payment'.

Subclause Y2.2 sets out time periods and circumstances to meet the requirements of Sections 110(1) and 110(2) of the Act. Section 110(1)(a) requires an 'adequate mechanism for determining what payments become due under the contract and when'. This mechanism is provided by the *Employer*'s notice to the *Consultant* in the third paragraph of Y2.2. This notice is to be issued not later than five days after the date when payment becomes due which is seven days after the assessment date. Section 110(1)(b) requires that there should be 'a final date for payment in relation to any sum which becomes due'. This is fourteen days, or the period stated in the Contract Data, after the date on which payment becomes due. The significance of the final date for payment is that if the *Employer* intends to withhold part of the amount due, he must give notice not later than a 'prescribed period', i.e. seven days before the final date for payment, as indicated in Section 111 of the Act.

Y2.4 Under Section 112 of the Act, where a sum due is not paid by the final date for payment and no effective notice to withhold payment has been given, the *Consultant* has a right to suspend performance. This right can only be exercised if the *Consultant* gives seven days' notice of his intention (subclause Y2.3). The right to suspend ceases when payment is made in full. Under Section 112(4) of the Act, the Completion Date is, in effect, delayed by the period of suspension. The effect of subclause Y2.4 is to treat such suspension as a compensation event. Thus, in addition to the extra time, the *Consultant* is entitled to additional costs resulting from the suspension.

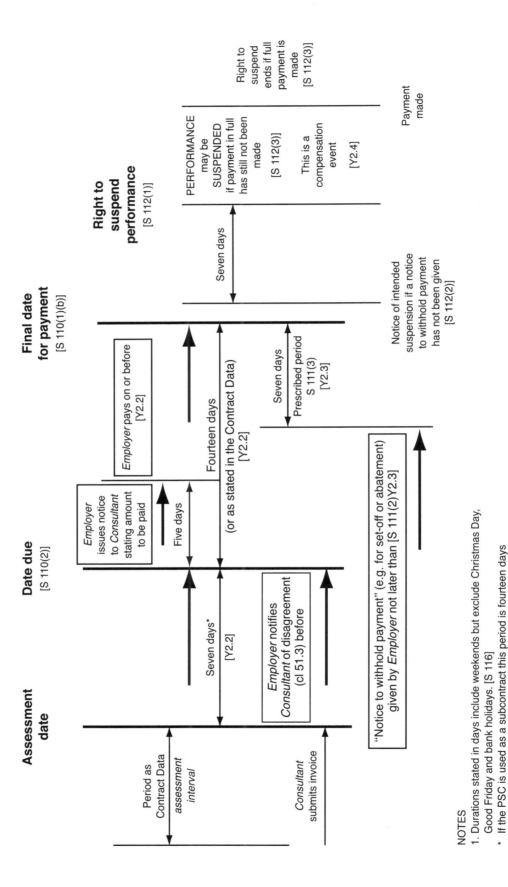
Assessment date

Date due
[S 110(2)]

Final date for payment
[S 110(1)(b)]

Right to suspend performance
[S 112(1)]

Period as Contract Data *assessment interval*

Seven days*
[Y2.2]

Employer issues notice to *Consultant* stating amount to be paid

Five days

Employer pays on or before
[Y2.2]

Fourteen days

(or as stated in the Contract Data)
[Y2.2]

Seven days

PERFORMANCE may be SUSPENDED if payment in full has still not been made
[S 112(3)]

This is a compensation event
[Y2.4]

Right to suspend ends if full payment is made
[S 112(3)]

Payment made

Employer notifies *Consultant* of disagreement (cl 51.3) before

Consultant submits invoice

Seven days Prescribed period S 111(3) [Y2.3]

Notice of intended suspension if a notice to withhold payment has not been given [S 112(2)]

"Notice to withhold payment" (e.g. for set-off or abatement) given by *Employer* not later than [S 111(2)Y2.3]

NOTES
1. Durations stated in days include weekends but exclude Christmas Day, Good Friday and bank holidays. [S 116]
* If the PSC is used as a subcontract this period is fourteen days (see also Appendices 3 and 4 of the guidance notes)

Figure 5. Construction Act – Payment periods under Y(UK)2.

Option Y(UK)3: The Contracts (Rights of Third Parties) Act 1999

Y3.1   If it is decided to give rights under the contract to a third party, it is important that the rights are clearly stated in the Contract Data by reference to clauses in the *conditions of contract*.

Option Z: *Additional conditions of contract*

This Option should be used where the *Employer* wishes to include additional conditions. These should be carefully drafted in the same style as the core and Option clauses using the same defined terms and other terminology. They should be carefully checked for consistency with the other conditions.

Additional conditions should be used only when absolutely necessary to accommodate particular needs, such as those peculiar to the country in which the work is to be done. The flexibility of the PSC main and secondary Options minimises the need for additional conditions. Additional conditions should not be used to limit how the *Consultant* is to do the work in the contract as this is part of the function of the Scope.

BASIS OF THE APPOINTMENT OF A *CONSULTANT*

The contract between the *Employer* and a *Consultant* will normally consist of

- a letter or form of offer from the *Consultant*,
- the Contract Data part one (completed by or in conjunction with the *Employer*),
- the Contract Data part two completed by the *Consultant*,
- an *activity schedule* (Options A and C) or a *task schedule* (Option G),
- the Scope,
- a letter of acceptance from the *Employer* and
- form of agreement (if any).

Contract Data

The purpose of the Contract Data for a particular contract is to identify the terms printed in italics in the conditions of contract (subclause 11.1) and to provide the information that some clauses state is in the Contract Data. The Contract Data thus completes the conditions for a particular contract.

Part one of the Contract Data is prepared by the *Employer* and identifies his requirements. The wording of the required statements is given in the PSC. This wording should be reproduced (but preferably not photocopied) with the various statements completed with the information relating to the particular contract.

Statements which must be included in all contracts are listed first, followed by optional statements. The introductory explanatory sentences (printed in bold) should be omitted. Only those statements which are needed for the particular contract should be included. In order to avoid lengthy entries for certain items it may be convenient to list them in a separate document, which can then be referenced in the Contract Data.

The completed part one of the document is normally issued to a consultant together with the prepared part two, which he is required to complete. It will identify other documents (e.g. *activity schedule*, *task schedule*) which are to be priced by the *Consultant* and submitted to the *Employer* with the completed part two of the Contract Data.

Further notes and a worked example of a completed Contract Data are given in Appendix 2.

Activity schedule (Options A and C)

This document is a list of the activities which the *Consultant* will need to carry out in order to Provide the Services. It should be prepared and priced by the *Consultant* but the *Employer* can include in his instructions to tenderers his required framework for the document or a list of the minimum items to be included.

The price entered by the *Consultant* for each activity is a lump sum, not a unit rate. In Option A the *Consultant* is paid for activities completed at each assessment date. In Option C, the total of the Prices in the *activity schedule* is the target price.

Task schedule (Option G)

The *task schedule* is prepared by the *Employer* and describes (in sufficient detail to enable the *Consultant* to price them) individual items which the *Employer* is likely to require the *Consultant* to carry out. Other items may be included in the *task schedule* to be paid for on a time basis using the Time Charge.

The *Consultant* prices each item in the *task schedule* which is not time based and quotes *staff rates* in part two of the Contract Data for use in calculating the Time Charge. When the *Employer* identifies a proposed Task he wishes to have carried out, he selects the required items from the *task schedule,* notifies any which are not on the *task schedule* as a compensation event and instructs the *Consultant* to submit his estimate for the Task. The *Consultant* does not carry out a Task until instructed to do so.

Scope

The conditions of contract refer to matters which must be covered by the Scope. These matters are summarised in Table 2.

In addition to the requirements made necessary by the particular contract, the Scope should contain further information describing what the *Consultant* is to provide. The extent of the Scope will vary between appointments. It will vary according to how well defined the *Employer*'s requirements are, what the particular *Consultant*'s tasks are and what function the *Consultant* is to perform.

Many professional bodies and organisations have prepared schedules of tasks, as have many employers' organisations. If assistance is needed in preparing the Scope, it will normally be appropriate to appoint a consultant for that purpose or to prepare it jointly with the selected *Consultant*.

Form of agreement

The creation of a contract can be by means of acceptance of a tender or a revised tender or by means of acceptance by the *Consultant* of a counter-offer prepared by or on behalf of the *Employer*. A binding contract is thus created, although some *Employers* may require such acceptance being subject to a formal agreement. A suitable form of agreement is included in Appendix 1, but *Employers* often have their own standard forms. Essentially, they record the agreement between the two Parties.

Table 2. References to the Scope in the PSC

This table does not include uses of the Scope not specifically required by the clauses, e.g. any specific levels of skill and care required (GN on subclause 21.2).

Subclause	Item	Comment
11.2(2) Identified and defined terms	Definition of Completion	Reference to Scope
11.2(5) Identified and defined terms	Definition of Defect	Reference to Scope
11.2(11)	Specifies and describes the *services*. States any constraints	General definition of Scope
13.6 Communications	Form of documents for retention	Form of retained copies stated in Scope, e.g. microfilm, originals
17.1 Illegal and impossible requirements	*Consultant* to notify	*Employer* to instruct changes to the Scope
20.2 The *Employer*'s obligations	*Employer* may change the Scope	Only the *Employer* can change the Scope
21.1 The *Consultant*'s obligations	Provides the Services	In accordance with the Scope
25.4 Other responsibilities	Health and safety requirements	In accordance with the Scope
31.2 The programme	Inclusions in programme	Dates constraining the work. List of activities to be carried out by the *Employer* and Others. Any specific information which the *Consultant* is to show on the programme, e.g. *key dates*, approvals
40.1 Quality management system	System requirements.	The Scope should describe what quality management system the *Consultant* will be required to operate
40.2 Quality management system	Information in quality plan	The Scope should identify any specific information to be shown in the quality plan and quality policy statement
50.2 Assessing the amount due	Details to be provided with the *Consultant*'s invoices	The *Employer* should set out any information he will require from the *Consultant* with each invoice to enable him to check the invoice for correctness
60.1(1) and (5) Compensation events	*Employer* changes Scope. *Employer* or Others do not work as stated in Scope	Compensation events related to Scope
63.10 Assessing compensation events	Proposed staff rates for change to Scope	*Consultant* to propose *staff rates* for people for whom there are no *staff rates*
70.1 The Parties' use of material	Use of material by the *Employer*.	The *Employer* must state the purposes for which he will be using any material provided by the *Consultant* (e.g. construction, maintenance, extension, rebuilding)
70.4 The Parties' use of material	*Consultant*'s use of materials for other work	'Other work' to be stated in the Scope
Option X4 X4.1 Parent company guarantee	Form of guarantee	If a guarantee is required, the *Employer* is to provide a pro-forma guarantee
Option X9 X9.1 Transfer of rights	Rights over material	Requirements stated in Scope
Option X13 X13.1 Performance bond	Form of bond	*Employer* to state form of bond

EXPLANATORY NOTES

1 General

CORE CLAUSES

Actions 10

10.1 This subclause states the general obligations of the Parties to act 'as stated in this contract'. Specific duties of the *Employer* and the *Consultant* and the procedures to be followed are stated elsewhere in the contract and are in the present tense, i.e. as at the time of the action, rather than in the form 'The *Consultant* shall...'. Where actions are permitted but not obligatory, the term 'may' is used.

The inclusion of the requirement on how the Parties should act, namely in a spirit of mutual trust and co-operation, is based on a recommendation in the Latham Report ('Constructing the Team'). This report, published in July 1994, was the final report of an investigation by Sir Michael Latham into procurement and contractual arrangements in the United Kingdom construction industry.

Identified and defined terms 11

11.1 The main definitions used in the contract are listed in subclause 11.2. Other definitions appear in optional clauses where they are specific to a particular Option. Capital initial letters are used in the PSC for defined terms to distinguish them from undefined terms. The same convention of italics and capital initials is used in these guidance notes as in the PSC itself.

11.2 (1) The definition of the Accepted Programme allows for the two situations where there may or may not have been a requirement for the *Consultant* to submit a programme with his tender. A tender programme is identified in the Contract Data and becomes the Accepted Programme when the contract comes into existence.

(2) The Scope must state what work is to be done before Completion can be certified under subclause 30.2. This, together with the second bullet, avoids the uncertainty associated with terms such as 'substantial completion'.

(3) The *completion date* stated in the Contract Data may be changed as a consequence of a compensation event.

(4) Contracts come into existence by various means – sometimes by means of a counter-offer and its acceptance, sometimes after extended negotiations and discussions. The Contract Date is used to define the date when the contract comes into existence, regardless of the means by which this is achieved.

It is very important to establish and document the means by which the contract came into existence. If this is not done, there is a significant risk of later difficulties if a dispute about the contract arises.

(5) A Defect is simply something which the *Employer* realises will not satisfy his requirements as stated in the Scope. This may be because the *Consultant* has not provided the *services* properly or it may be that the initial Scope did not accurately reflect the *Employer*'s intentions and therefore has to be changed under subclause 20.2, triggering a compensation event under subclause 60.1(1). Clause 41 (Correcting Defects) deals further with the consequences of a Defect.

(6) Key Dates are different from Completion Dates for a *section* of the *services* as in Option X5. They are dates by which the *services* are required to reach a stated Condition. The *Employer* has the authority to change a Key Date, and such a change is a compensation event (subclauses 20.2 and 60.1(4)). The consequences of failure by the *Consultant* to meet a Key Date are set out in subclause 23.3.

(7) The defined term 'Others' provides a convenient means of reference (by stating the exceptions) to people and organisations not directly involved in the contract.

(9) & These subclauses define the two key terms used in subclause 21.1 to state
(11) what the *Consultant* is to do under the contract.

Within both definitions, a broad title of the *services* would be identified in the Contract Data, e.g. 'project management of the construction of a new factory at Swindon'.

The *Employer* should use the Scope to specify and describe the *services* as comprehensively as possible, including what he is expecting to achieve as a result of the contract and a statement of any constraints which the *Consultant* is to abide by.

The clauses of the PSC contain many references to information and requirements which should be specified in the Scope. These are summarised in Table 2. The *Employer* can change the Scope during the course of the contract (subclause 20.2).

(10) The Risk Register provides a means of identifying the risks and managing them by eliminating them or reducing them, or otherwise deciding how they are to be dealt with. Subclause 15.4 provides a procedure for revising the register following a risk reduction meeting.

(13) The Time Charge is defined in relation to *staff rates* and staff time expended on the *services*. For many commissions the entries for *staff rates* in part two of the Contract Data will have fixed hourly, weekly or monthly rates entered against them. On other occasions, the *staff rates* will need to be defined in relation to salary.

The Time Charge is used in the PSC in two ways

- for assessment of compensation events for all Options and
- for evaluation of the amount due to the *Consultant* for the *services* in Option E (time based contract), Option C (target contract) and partially in Option G (term contract).

The *staff rates* are effectively the price charged for staff on a time basis. They will include for all costs to the *Consultant* including basic salary, any additional payments or benefits and social costs such as insurances or pension payments. Office expenses, including rental and heating, non-recoverable staff time and administrative staff who are not chargeable, together with the *Consultant*'s general overheads and profit, should also be allowed for in the *staff rates*.

The *staff rates* can conveniently be established in one of three ways

- rates for named staff,
- rates for categories of staff or
- rates related to salaries paid to staff.

The choice between these alternatives will depend on the type of *services* to be carried out. Where the *services* are to be provided by one person or a few staff identified in advance, individual rates for those staff would be most appropriate. If it becomes necessary to change staff, a new rate is readily negotiated based on different salary and other matters. Rate adjustments for inflation, if necessary, can be based either on actual salary adjustments or by using Option X1: Price adjustment for inflation.

If the *services* are to be carried out by a larger number of staff, but having clearly defined duties or responsibilities, the second method of defining *staff rates* is appropriate. The services of the supervisor on a large site is an example. The various posts can readily be categorised, and hourly, daily or weekly rates given for staff in each category. If price adjustment for inflation is needed, Option X1 is used.

If neither of these methods is suitable, *staff rates* should be linked to salary. This method has wide application and does not artificially reduce or increase the payments made. The difficulties of categorisation are avoided, but care needs to be taken to define which staff time is recoverable and which is not. The *staff rates* would then be stated as a multiplier on salary.

In this third method, the *Employer* has least control over costs. Under Options C, E and G, provision is made for forecasts at specified intervals by the *Consultant*, with explanations of changes since the last forecast (subclause 21.5).

Many *Employers* have their own model for defining salaries and multipliers for staff and for identifying who may allocate time and who is included in the multiplier.

Communications 13

13.1 The phrase 'in a form which can be read, copied and recorded' includes a letter sent by post, telex, cable, electronic mail, facsimile transmission, and on disc, magnetic tape or similar electronic means.

13.3 Unless the contract states a period for reply to a particular communication, a reply has to be made within the *period for reply*. Where a variety of different communications is to be handled, e.g. requests for information, acceptance of contractors' designs, general correspondence, different *periods for reply* may be necessary. If so, they can be separately listed in the Contract Data.

13.4 (13.8) The PSC contains a number of situations in which the *Employer* must either accept or reject a document which contains proposals submitted by the *Consultant*. The *Consultant* carries the risk of the *Employer* withholding acceptance because the proposal does not comply with the Scope or for a reason stated in the contract. Withholding acceptance for any other reason is a compensation event (subclause 60.1(8)). This arrangement gives the *Employer* freedom to withhold acceptance for any reason but limits the *Consultant's* risk associated with this freedom. The *Employer* should ensure that the Scope states his requirements clearly, especially in areas which could directly affect his interests, e.g. his procurement strategy for further contracts for design, supply, construction, etc.

13.5 This subclause provides for extending the *period for reply* by agreement.

13.6 The *Employer* must decide the period during which the *Consultant* must keep the various documents he has used in doing his work. This period is entered in part one of the Contract Data.

13.7 The requirement to separate notifications from other communications is included to avoid important matters being missed.

Early warning 15

15.1 The intention of this subclause is to oblige each Party to warn the other of anything which could affect the outcome of the contract as expressed in the six bullets and then to promote co-operation between the Parties to mitigate any adverse effects. Early warning matters are recorded in the Risk Register.

An early warning may often be associated with the notification of a future compensation event. For instance, the *Consultant* may give early warning of a probable change in the law (Option X2) and notify a compensation event at the same time. However, if the change is only a possibility, an early warning on its own may be appropriate and the notification of a compensation event deferred. Where a compensation event has already been notified, an early warning notice is not necessary.

In contrast, the *Employer* may instruct a change in the Scope and notify it as a compensation event under subclause 60.1(1). Both Parties are then aware of the instruction, assessments will be provided under the compensation event procedure and no early warning should be necessary.

Subclauses 61.5 and 63.5 provide a sanction for failure by the *Consultant* to give early warning of a matter when he became aware of it by reducing the payment due to him for any related compensation events.

It is probable that the *Employer* will require additional reporting by the *Consultant* – for example on any changes to potential construction costs. Such additional requirements should be stated in the Scope.

15.2 15.3	These subclauses provide a procedure for the Parties to meet following an early warning and to co-operate in finding solutions and deciding actions.
15.4	Decisions made at the risk reduction meeting are recorded in the Risk Register.

Ambiguities and inconsistencies 16

16.1 This subclause is intended to ensure that action is taken as soon as possible to deal with ambiguities and inconsistencies which are noticed in the contract documents. There is no stated precedence of documents and the *Employer* has the responsibility of instructing resolution of the problem. An instruction which results in a change to the Scope or a change to a previous decision would be a compensation event (subclause 60.1 (1) or (7)). Also, in Option G, an instruction which corrects a mistake in the Task Schedule is a compensation event under subclause 60.2.

Illegal and impossible requirements 17

17.1 A change to the Scope in order to resolve a matter which requires the *Consultant* to do anything which is illegal or impossible is a compensation event (subclause 60.1(1)).

Prevention 18

18.1 This subclause is designed to deal with what is commonly referred to as 'force majeure' events, that is, the kind of events which neither Party can prevent or control.

MAIN OPTION CLAUSES

Option G: Term contract

Identified and defined terms 11

11.2 (21) Work is carried out by the *Consultant* only after the *Employer* has instructed a Task under subclause 55.5.

The other main Option clauses in Section 1 are definitions concerning payment. Guidance on these is included in Section 5.

2 The Parties' main responsibilities

This section sets out the *Employer*'s and the *Consultant*'s main responsibilities. Other sections deal with particular responsibilities appropriate to the section heading.

CORE CLAUSES

The *Employer*'s obligations 20

20.1 This subclause relates to the compensation events stated in subclause 60.1(3).

20.2 The authority to change the Scope or a Key Date belongs exclusively to the *Employer*. Neither the *Consultant* nor the *Adjudicator* can change these.

20.3 This subclause recognises the professional nature of the *services* being provided. If the *Employer*'s instructions cannot be complied with, the *Consultant* should advise the *Employer* of the fact and suggest alternative measures to achieve the *Employer*'s requirements.

The *Consultant*'s obligations 21

21.1 This subclause states the *Consultant*'s basic obligation.

21.2 This subclause states the level of skill and care required of the *Consultant*. It follows that a Defect may not necessarily be the liability of the *Consultant*.

People 22

22.1 The *key persons* named in the Contract Data should be the persons named by the *Consultant* and accepted by the *Employer* to do the jobs most critical to Providing the Services. The *Consultant* does not have the right to replace a *key person* at will and can only replace him if the replacement is acceptable to the *Employer*. If the *Employer*'s reason for not accepting a proposed replacement for a *key person* is not the reason stated in this subclause, a compensation event occurs (subclause 60.1(8)).

Working with the *Employer* and Others 23

23.1 The duty of the *Consultant* to co-operate with Others has been expressed in the PSC in general terms only.

23.2 On large projects there may be several consultants and other organisations Details of these and the services they are required to provide should be stated in the Scope. On some projects the lead consultant, who is responsible for co-ordinating the work of all other consultants, should also be identified in the Scope.

It is important that planning and programming of the work of the various consultants and Others are carried out before the start of the contract. The *Consultant* is not responsible for the failure of other parties to carry out their work in accordance with the Accepted Programme unless the failure is caused by the *Consultant* not co-operating. The exchange of information on health and safety matters is particularly important in order to comply with the law as well as with the contract.

23.3 This subclause provides the *Employer* with a remedy when the *Consultant* fails to meet a Key Date. It is limited to the additional cost incurred by the *Employer*, as stated.

Subconsulting 24

24.1   These subclauses permit the *Consultant* to arrange for parts of the *services* to
to   be provided by Subconsultants, provided the *Employer* accepts the proposed
24.3   Subconsultant and the subcontract conditions to be used. Acceptance of the
Subconsultant cannot be withdrawn later, providing his appointment complies
with these subclauses, but the *Consultant* is responsible for the Subconsultant's performance under subclause 24.1.

The PSC may be used by a *Consultant* to appoint a Subconsultant if it is
adapted as explained in Appendix 4.

Other responsibilities 25

25.1   The *Employer* should state in the Scope what approvals he has obtained.
Under this subclause the *Consultant* is required to obtain any other approvals
which are necessary. If the *Consultant* is required to report on the status of
the approvals he is required to obtain, this should also be stated in the
Scope. If for some reason obtaining approvals is delayed, the *Consultant* (or
Employer) should give early warning under subclause 15.1 and the Accepted
Programme may need to be changed. If approvals cannot be obtained, e.g.
planning permission is refused, the *Consultant* should notify the *Employer* of
an illegality or impossibility under subclause 17.1, after which action lies with
the *Employer*.

25.2   Where the *Consultant* needs access to a person, place or thing in order to
Provide the Services, the *Employer* is required to provide it by an *access date*
in accordance with the contract.

Provision is made in part one of the Contract Data for the *Employer* to list the
accesses which the *Consultant* will need and state the *access date* which has
been arranged for each.

Provision is also made in part two of the Contract Data for the *Consultant* to
state any additional accesses he will require together with the relevant *access
dates*.

During the course of the contract, access dates later than those stated in the
Contract Data may be agreed by the Parties and included in the Accepted
Programme. A compensation event is triggered under subclause 60.1(2) if an
access is provided late.

25.4   Any specific health and safety requirements related to the *Consultant*'s
activities in providing the *services* should be stated in the Scope. These are
additional to any obligations the *Consultant* may have under national law.

MAIN OPTION CLAUSES

Option A: Priced contract with activity schedule

The *Consultant*'s 21
obligations 21.3   Forecasts of the total *expenses* are required for budget purposes, updated at
regular intervals. They enable the *Employer* to judge the likely final cost to him
of *expenses* which are additional to the Prices.

Option C: Target contract

The *Consultant*'s **21**
obligations 21.4 Forecasts of the total Time Charge and *expenses* are required for budget purposes. They enable the *Employer* to judge the likely final Price for Services Provided to Date, the likely *Consultant*'s share and the likely cost to him of *expenses.* Forecasts are updated at regular intervals.

Option E: Time based contract

The *Consultant*'s **21**
obligations 21.4 Forecasts of the total Time Charge and *expenses* are required for budget purposes. They enable the *Employer* to judge the likely final cost to him of the *services*. Forecasts are updated at regular intervals.

Option G: Term contract

The *Consultant*'s **21**
obligations 21.4 Forecasts of the total Time Charge and *expenses* are required for budget purposes. They enable the *Employer* to judge the likely final cost to him of the time based items and the *expenses* for the Tasks instructed before the date of the forecast. The lump sum prices for the other items in the Tasks are additional to the forecasts.

3 Time

CORE CLAUSES

Starting, Completion and Key Dates **30**

30.1 The Completion Date (defined in subclause 11.2(3)) may be of minor importance in some professional services contracts, but in others it can be critical in co-ordinating the work of several consultants.

Provision is made in the Contract Data for the *completion date*

- to be specified by the *Employer* in part one or
- to be tendered by the *Consultant* in part two.

The Completion Date may be changed from the *completion date* as a result of a compensation event.

It is essential that a *completion date* is stated in the contract in either part one or part two of the Contract Data. If this is not done, the time effects of compensation events cannot be applied.

30.2 The *Employer* is responsible for certifying Completion, as defined in subclause 11.2(2), within one week of it being achieved.

The programme **31**

31.1 Provision is made for a programme either agreed at the Contract Date or to be prepared by the *Consultant* and submitted at an early stage in the contract. In the latter event the *Employer* is required to respond within two weeks (subclause 31.3), but if the reply is non-acceptance, the *Consultant* is required to re-submit within the *period for reply*.

The Accepted Programme as defined in subclause 11.2(1) is an important document for administering the contract. It enables the *Employer* and the *Consultant* to monitor progress and to assess the effects of compensation events. It identifies when particular actions are needed from the Parties.

31.2 This subclause lists the information which the *Consultant* is required to show on each programme submitted for acceptance. Further information to be shown on the programme for a specific contract should be stated in the Scope (see Table 2).

The *starting date* is the date when the *Consultant* can start work on the *services* and is used in subclause 50.1 to fix the payment assessment dates throughout the contract.

31.3 This subclause gives the reasons why an *Employer* may decide not to accept a programme. Any failure by the *Employer* to accept a programme for reasons other than those stated in this subclause is a compensation event unless the programme does not comply with the Scope (subclause 60.1(8)).

Revising the programme **32**

32.1 This subclause lists the matters which are to be shown on a revised programme. It should record the actual progress achieved on each operation and the re-programming of future operations. It should also show the effects of implemented compensation events and early warning matters. If a compensation event affects the timing of future operations, a revised programme indicating the effects is to be submitted as part of the alterations or even a *Consultant*'s quotation (subclause 62.2). The alterations to or the revised programme should also show proposals for dealing with delays, Defects and any changes proposed by the *Consultant*.

Instructions to stop or not to start work	**33**
	33.1 This subclause gives the *Employer* authority to control the stopping and re-starting of the *Consultant*'s work for any reason. An instruction given under this subclause constitutes a compensation event, but if it arises from a fault of the *Consultant*, the Prices are not changed (subclause 61.4).
Acceleration	**34**
	34.1
	34.2 Acceleration means bringing the Completion Date forward. This differs from usage in many contracts where 'acceleration' means speeding up the work to ensure that the Completion Date is achieved. These subclauses allow the *Employer* to obtain a quotation from the *Consultant* for acceleration. There is no remedy if it is not produced. Acceleration can only be achieved by agreement between the Parties. It cannot be imposed on the *Consultant* without his agreement.

MAIN OPTION CLAUSES

Option A: Priced contract with activity schedule

The programme **31**

31.4 This subclause enables the timing of payments to be related to the programme.

Option C: Target contract

The programme **31**

31.4 This subclause relates the make-up of the Prices (the target) to the programme.

Option G: Term contract

The programme **31**

31.5 This subclause enables the timing of payments within each Task to be related to the programme.

4 Quality

CORE CLAUSES

Quality management system **40**

40.1 to 40.3   These subclauses provide for the *Consultant* to operate a quality management system to the extent required by the Scope.

The *Employer* decides the extent of the quality management system. On one extreme he may require no quality management system at all. On the other extreme he may require the operation of a fully certified quality assurance system under ISO standards. The quality management system required of the *Consultant* should recognise the equivalent requirements on other consultants or contractors and be compatible with them.

If the *Consultant* fails to provide the quality statement and quality plan as required by the Scope (subclause 40.2), the *Employer* may, as a last resort, terminate the *Consultant*'s appointment in accordance with subclause 90.3.

Correcting Defects **41**

41.1   The period between Completion and the *defects date* is stated in the Contract Data. The length of the period will depend on the type of services being provided, but will normally be between six months and a year. This subclause requires each Party to notify the other of each Defect found until the *defects date.* The *Consultant* is required to notify uncorrected Defects at Completion (subclause 11.2(2)) and any new Defects he becomes aware of after Completion and until the *defects date*, which is the cut-off date for the *Consultant*'s responsibility to correct. The final sentence preserves the *Employer*'s rights in relation to Defects which are not discovered until after the *defects date*.

41.2   This subclause requires the *Consultant* to correct all Defects, i.e. so that the *services* are in accordance with the Scope (subclause 11.2(5)). It does not require any admission by the *Consultant* of responsibility for the Defect but enables the *services* to be corrected with appropriate urgency to minimise disruption to the *Employer*'s project (see Figure 6). Correction by the *Consultant* of a Defect for which he is not liable under the contract constitutes a compensation event (subclause 60.1(12)). This subclause also states the action that the *Employer* may take if the *Consultant* fails to correct a Defect in accordance with the contract.

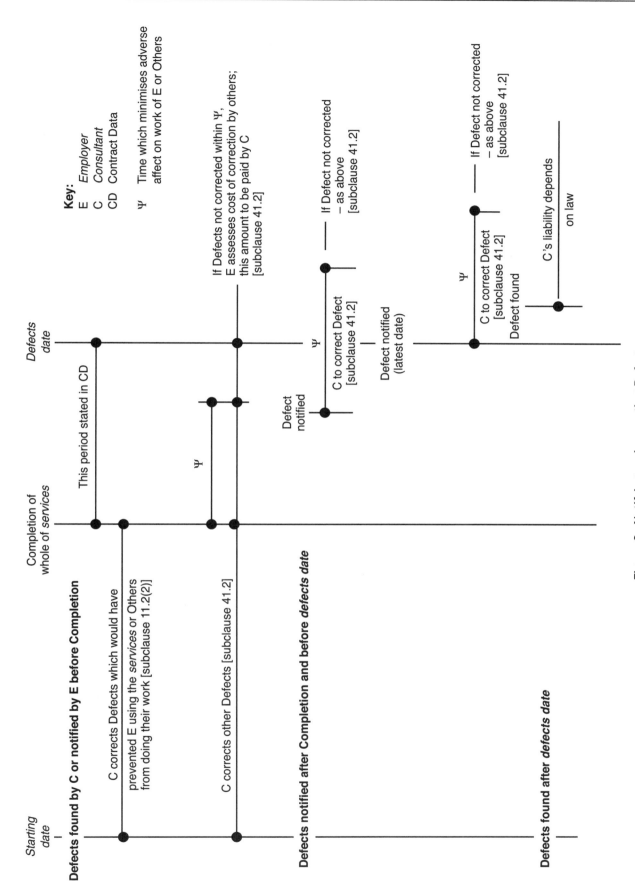

Figure 6. Notifying and correcting Defects.

5 Payment

The payment mechanisms for the four main Options are distinguished mainly by the use of two key terms

- the Prices and
- the Price for Services Provided to Date.

Each term is defined in subclause 11.2 for each main Option.

The Prices

Option A (11.2(18))	The lump sum prices for each of the activities in the Activity Schedule.
Option C (11.2(18))	As Option A.
Option E (11.2(19))	The Time Charge.
Option G (11.2(20))	The Time Charge for items described as time based on the Task Schedule and the lump sum price in the Task Schedule for each other item.

The Price for Services Provided to Date

Option A (11.2(15))	The *Consultant* is paid the lump sum prices for activities from the Activity Schedule which have been completed at the assessment date. It is important that the *Consultant*, when compiling the *activity schedule*, defines activities, completion of which can be clearly recognised.
Option C (11.2(16))	Payment to the *Consultant* is as Option E. The Prices are the target and are compared with the Time Charge at the time of final payment to determine the *Consultant*'s share (clause 54).
Option E (11.2(16))	The *Consultant* is paid the Time Charge for *services* carried out.
Option G (11.2(17))	The *Consultant* is paid, for each Task, the Time Charge for time based work completed and a proportion of the lump sums representing the proportion of work completed.

The following notes on Section 5 apply to the general and international use of the PSC. The key periods affecting the procedure for payments are illustrated in Figure 7, which should be referred to in conjunction with the notes.

On contracts in the United Kingdom to which the Housing Grants, Construction and Regeneration Act 1996 Part II applies, Option Y(UK)2 should be incorporated. Reference should then be made to the separate notes on Option Y(UK)2, which include references to the necessary modifications and additions to core clauses.

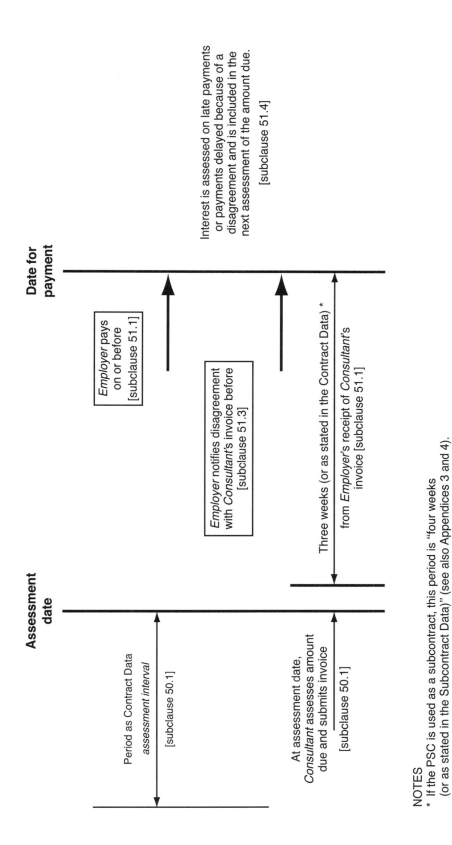

Figure 7. Payment Periods.

NOTES
* If the PSC is used as a subcontract, this period is "four weeks (or as stated in the Subcontract Data)" (see also Appendices 3 and 4).

CORE CLAUSES

Assessing the amount due 50

50.1 This subclause determines the assessment dates. The subsequent dates when payment is due are calculated from the date when the *Employer* receives the *Consultant*'s invoice (subclause 51.1). The first assessment date is decided by the *Consultant*, preferably after discussion with the *Employer*, to suit the internal procedures of both Parties. The *Employer* states the *assessment interval* in the Contract Data. The first main bullet determines the final assessment date which allows time for the correction of any Defects notified just before the *defects date* and subsequently for the assessment of the payment due from the *Consultant* of any Defects which remain uncorrected (subclause 41.2).

50.2 The *Consultant* is required to make an assessment of the amount due at each assessment date. He is required to submit an invoice for the change in the amount due since the previous invoice and provide the details stated in the Scope to show how the amount due has been calculated.

50.3 The main part of the amount due is the Price for Services Provided to Date, as defined for each main Option in subclause 11.2.

Expenses

The amount due also includes the *expenses* incurred by the *Consultant* in Providing the Services. The items of *expenses* are defined in part one and part two of the Contract Data. The *Employer* should complete part one for any *expenses* for which he wishes to state the amount to be paid. The *Consultant* should complete part two for any additional *expenses* and the amount of payment he requires. Any expenses not so defined are not reimbursed to the *Consultant*, who must therefore make due allowance for them in pricing his offer, i.e. in the lump sums, *staff rates*, etc. Only *expenses* stated in the Contract Data are payable in addition to the Price for Services Provided to Date in all payment options.

Items of *expenses* which may be included in the Contract Data are photocopies, telephone, facsimile and package costs, postage, travel and hotel costs. Details of travel costs by public transport or private car should also be included as required.

Expenses should also include disbursements, which are fees and charges paid by the *Consultant* on behalf of the *Employer*. Any such items which the *Employer* requires the *Consultant* to arrange for and pay, e.g. fees for planning applications or advertising for site staff, should be listed as *expenses* in the Contract Data.

Pricing of *expenses* may be expressed in various forms. These include

- at net cost
- at cost plus . . . . percent
- lump sums and rates
- percentage of the Prices.

Payment 51

51.1 Set-off is not specifically mentioned in this subclause. Thus if the *Employer* has a legitimate claim against the *Consultant* the normal law of set-off will apply.

51.3 Where the *Employer* is not in agreement with an invoice submitted by the *Consultant*, he has to

- pay the amount he does not dispute and
- explain to the *Consultant* why and where he disagrees.

The *Consultant* then has to correct the invoice to the *Employer*'s assessment or provide further information to justify the invoice already submitted. While the disagreement is being resolved the *Employer* should pay what he considers the proper amount in respect of the *services* provided. This will include substituting his assessment for the *Consultant*'s invoice in respect of that part of the *services* he disagrees with. If he fails to make payment he will be liable to pay interest to the *Consultant* on any delayed payment (subclause 51.4).

51.5   The *interest rate* stated in part one of the Contract Data should comprise a reliable annual base rate applicable to the territory in which the work is to be done plus a percentage (recommended to be at least 2%) to represent the current commercial rates. Simple interest at the *interest rate* applies for periods of less than one year.

MAIN OPTION CLAUSES

Option A: Priced contract with activity schedule

Accounts and records   **52**

51.1   This subclause requires the *Consultant* to keep records of *expenses* and entitles the *Employer* to inspect them if he so wishes.

The Activity Schedule   **53**

53.2   An *activity schedule* which contains items which do not represent the *Consultant*'s proposed activities and methods of working will create difficulties in determining payments due. Thus it is important that the Activity Schedule should relate directly to the programme (also subclause 31.4) and always be compatible with it.

53.3   This subclause states the reasons which the *Employer* can give for not accepting changes to the Activity Schedule (in addition to non-compliance with the Scope) without creating a compensation event (subclause 60.1 (8)). For instance, any change in Prices should not upset the balance of pricing which existed in the original Activity Schedule. The total of the Prices must not be changed except by implemented compensation events.

Option C: Target contract

Accounts and records   **52**

52.2   This subclause requires the *Consultant* to keep records of Time Charge and *expenses* and entitles the *Employer* to inspect them if he so wishes.

The Activity Schedule   **53**

53.2   It is important that the Activity Schedule should relate directly to the programme and always be compatible with it.

53.3   This subclause states the reasons which the *Employer* can give for not accepting changes to the Activity Schedule (in addition to non-compliance with the Scope) without creating a compensation event (subclause 60.1(8)). For instance, any change in Prices should not upset the balance of pricing which existed in the original Activity Schedule. The total of the Prices must not be changed except by implemented compensation events.

The *Consultant*'s share   **54**

54.1   Subclause 54.1 states how the *Consultant*'s share is calculated. Subclause
54.2   54.2 states the main principle of target contracts whereby the *Consultant* receives a share of any saving and pays a share of any excess when the final Price for Services Provided to Date (PSPD) (Time Charge) is compared to the target (the total of the Prices).

For example, assume that the Contract Data states that

- The *Consultant*'s *share percentages* and the *share ranges* are

Share range	Consultant's share percentage
less than 80%	15%
from 80% to 90%	30%
from 90% to 110%	50%
greater than 110%	20%

If at Completion of the whole of the *services* the total of the Prices (having been adjusted for compensation events) is £100,000, the Contract Data table becomes in effect

Final PSPD	Consultant's share percentage
less than £80,000	15%
from £80,000 to £90,000	30%
from £90,000 to £110,000	50%
greater than £110,000	20%

Examples of possible outcomes are

a) Final PSPD = £75,000
Saving under total of the Prices = £25,000
Comprising three increments

less than £80,000	= £5,000 @ 15%	= £750
£80,000 to £90,000	= £10,000 @ 30%	= £3,000
£90,000 to £110,000	= £10,000 @ 50%	= £5,000
Consultant's share (paid by *Employer*)		= £8,750

b) Final PSPD = £95,000
Saving under total of the Prices = £5,000
Comprising one increment

£90,000 to £110,000	= £5,000 @ 50%	= £2,500
Consultant's share (paid by *Employer*)		= £2,500

c) Final PSPD = £115,000
Excess over total of the Prices = £15,000
Comprising two increments

£90,000 to £110,000	= £10,000 @ 50%	= £5,000
greater than £110,000	= £5,000 @ 20%	= £1,000
Consultant's share (paid to *Employer*)		= £6,000

The other potential source of profit for the *Consultant* is within the *staff rates* used to calculate the Time Charge. The *Consultant*'s *share percentages* should be determined in a particular contract to provide the appropriate level of incentive to the *Consultant* to minimise the final PSPD. The extent of financial risk to the Parties in the event of the final PSPD exceeding the total of the Prices, can be varied between two extremes.

- A guaranteed maximum price to the *Employer* can be achieved by stating the *Consultant*'s *share percentage* to be 100% above that price.
- A limit to the deduction from the total Time Charge (the final PSPD) paid to the *Consultant* can be achieved by stating the *Consultant*'s *share percentage* to be 0% above a stated share range.

Reference should be made to CIRIA Report 85 for further information and guidance on the working of target contracts.

54.3
54.4

Payment of the *Consultant*'s share is made in two stages. Firstly, a preliminary assessment is included in the payment due following Completion of the whole of the *services*. Secondly, a final assessment is included in the final payment made after the *defects date*.

Interim payments of the *Consultant*'s share are not provided for. There are two main reasons for this.

- The Prices tendered by a Consultant have the main purpose of establishing the total of the Prices (the target). It is not intended that their build-up should provide a realistic forecast of cash flow. They are therefore unlikely to be comparable with the PSPD at any interim stage.
- Forecasts of both the final PSPD (Time Charge) and the final total of the Prices would be extremely uncertain at early stages of the contract. Any delays in assessing compensation events would further distort the calculation.

The danger of serious underpayment or overpayment of an interim *Consultant*'s share has therefore led to the policy of an estimated payment on Completion which is corrected at assessment of the final amount due.

Nevertheless, provision is made in subclause 92.3 for the assessment of the *Consultant*'s share if there is a termination.

Option E: Time based contract

Accounts and records **52**

52.2
This subclause requires the *Consultant* to keep records of Time Charge and *expenses* and entitles the *Employer* to inspect them if he so wishes.

Option G: Term contract

Accounts and records **52**

52.2
This subclause requires the *Consultant* to keep records of Time Charge and *expenses* and entitles the *Employer* to inspect them if he so wishes.

Assessing Tasks **55**

55.1
The actions to be taken by the *Employer* to initiate the assessment of a proposed Task are stated in this subclause.

If all the items in the proposed Task are on the *task schedule*, the *Consultant*'s estimate will be straightforward. It is therefore most important that the *task schedule* prepared by the *Employer* to be priced by the *Consultant* in his bid is as comprehensive as possible in the list of items of services which the *Employer* is likely to require to be carried out.

However, if a proposed Task includes items not on the *task schedule*, these items are assessed as compensation events – subclause 55.2.

55.2
This subclause states how delay damages are assessed. Note that delay damages can be introduced into a Task Order if Option X7 has been included in the contract.

6 Compensation events

Compensation events are events stated in the contract which, if they occur, entitle the *Consultant* to be compensated for any effect which the event has on the Prices and on the Accepted Programme (subclause 62.2). The assessment of a compensation event is always based on its effect on both the Time Charge and on the Accepted Programme. Compensation events may entitle the *Consultant* to additional payment and possibly additional time in which to carry out the *services*. In some specific cases they may result in a reduced payment to the *Consultant*.

CORE CLAUSES

Compensation events 60.1

Changing the Scope (1)

Variations to the *services* are effected by an *Employer*'s instruction to change the Scope. The authority given to the *Employer* to make such changes is covered by subclause 20.2. A change to the Scope may amend some detail of the *services* to be provided or impose a change in the way the *services* are to be carried out.

When Option G has been chosen the *Employer* should state in his instruction whether a change to the Scope applies generally to the affected items in the Task Schedule or only to the items in a particular Task.

Failure to provide access (2)

This compensation event arises when the *Employer* fails to provide access in accordance with subclause 25.2.

Failure by the *Employer* or Others (5)

Although the *Consultant* is required to co-operate with Others, if necessary by arranging meetings with them (subclauses 23.1, 23.2), any failure by them to perform constitutes a compensation event. Thus a failure by a service company not subcontracted to the *Consultant* to provide details of its services in time would constitute a compensation event. The *Employer* will define in the Scope the extent of the interface between the *Consultant* and Others and the extent to which the *Consultant* is entitled to rely upon the performance of Others.

Withholding acceptance (8)

Various clauses give reasons why the *Employer* may not accept a submission or a proposal from the *Consultant*. Withholding acceptance for any other reason is a compensation event.

Correction of an assumption (9)

Under subclause 61.6 (see later notes) the *Employer* may state assumptions to be used in assessing a compensation event. If he later notifies a correction to these assumptions, the notification is a separate compensation event.

Employer's breach of contract (10)

This is an 'umbrella' clause to include breaches of contract by the *Employer* within the compensation event procedure.

Unforeseen events (11)

The events listed in this subclause sometimes come into the category of 'force majeure' in certain jurisdictions. The *Employer* carries the financial risk of such events.

Correcting Defects (12)

Not all Defects are the *Consultant*'s liability under this contract. Those Defects which arise notwithstanding the fact that the *Consultant* has exercised the skill and care described in subclause 21.2 are the *Employer*'s responsibility. Correction of these Defects is a compensation event.

Notifying compensation **61**

events 61.1 This procedure would apply to those compensation events which are due to an action of the *Employer*. When the event occurs, the *Employer* notifies the *Consultant* and instructs him to submit quotations. Where the compensation events results from the *Consultant*'s fault or where quotations have already been submitted, quotations are not instructed. However, in order to avoid doubt in such cases, it is advisable that when the *Employer* notifies the compensation event, he should give his reason for not instructing quotations. The *Consultant* is required to act on the instruction or changed decision.

61.2 This subclause deals with the situation where the *Employer* is considering issuing an instruction or changing a decision but first requires to know what effect this would have on the Prices and the Accepted Programme – for example when he is considering a change to the Scope under subclause 60.1(1). He has the authority to instruct the *Consultant* to submit quotations as a first step.

61.3 This procedure would normally apply to the compensation events not covered by those in subclause 61.1. These are events which arise from

- a failure by the *Employer* to fulfil his obligations,
- the *Employer* withholding an acceptance for a reason not stated in the contract or
- a happening not caused by either Party.

It would also apply to an event which the *Employer* has not notified under subclause 61.1.

In such cases the *Consultant* initiates the procedure by notifying the *Employer*.

The stated time limit is intended to expedite the procedure so that dealing with compensation events a long time after they have occurred is avoided. The wording of this clause has been amended because in the second edition the two week period was too short to be realistic in some cases and as stated it did not prevent late notification of compensation events.

61.4 This subclause lists four tests which the *Employer* applies to an event notified by the *Consultant* in order to decide whether or not to instruct the *Consultant* to submit quotations. If the *Employer* decides that the event does not pass any one of the tests he notifies the *Consultant* and no further action is required unless the *Consultant* disputes the decision and refers it to the *Adjudicator* under the dispute resolution Option. The subclause also states a procedure which provides for a situation where the *Employer* fails to respond within the time limits stated. The *Consultant* may notify the *Employer* accordingly, which effectively provides the *Employer* with a two week 'period of grace' to respond. If this produces no action from the *Employer*, the event notified by the *Consultant* is deemed to be a compensation event.

61.5 The *Employer* should include in an instruction to submit quotations, his decision on whether or not the *Consultant* gave an early warning which an experienced consultant could have given.

61.6 In some cases, the nature of the compensation event may be such that it is impossible to prepare a sufficiently accurate quotation. In these cases, quotations are submitted on the basis of assumptions stated by the *Employer* in his instruction to the *Consultant*. If the assumptions later prove to be wrong, the *Employer*'s notification of their correction is a separate compensation event (subclause 60.1(9)).

Apart from this situation, the assessment of compensation events cannot be revised (subclause 65.2). The reason for this strict procedure is to motivate the Parties to decide the effects of each compensation event either before or soon after it occurs. Since each quotation can include due allowance for risk (subclause 63.6) and since the early warning procedure should minimise the effects of unexpected problems, the need for later review is minimal.

Quotations for	**62**	
compensation events	62.1	There may be several ways of dealing with a compensation event and its consequences. The procedure in this subclause enables the *Employer* to consider different options. For instance it may be more beneficial to the *Employer* to have the *services* carried out under the existing programme at a greater cost than an alternative of delaying the *services* but at a lower cost. Quotations include both time and money implications as, in most situations, it is impossible to consider each in isolation.

62.2   Quotations are based on an assessment of Time Charge and time arising from the compensation event. A build-up of each quotation is to be submitted by the *Consultant*. If re-programming of remaining work is required, the quotation should include alterations to the Accepted Programme.

62.3   The time limits are intended to promote efficient management of the contract procedures. The four categories of reply by the *Employer* are listed. The third category may result from the *Employer* deciding not to proceed with a proposed change to the Scope. This may happen when the cost of the change is too high or the delay too great. The *Employer* has absolute discretion in such a case on whether to proceed. The fourth category applies when the *Employer* decides that the *Consultant*'s quotation is not acceptable.

62.4   This procedure permits revision of quotations. In practice this will usually follow discussion between the *Employer* and the *Consultant* on the details of the submitted quotations. Again, a time limit for submission of the revised quotations is stated.

62.5   This provision permits extension of the time for submitting quotations. It would be used where the consequences of a compensation event may be complex.

62.6   The procedure in this subclause is designed to deal with a situation where the *Employer* does not reply within the time stated in the contract or a longer agreed time. Failure by the *Employer* to respond to a quotation within the stated time results in 'deemed' acceptance.

Assessing compensation	**63**	
events	63.1	Assessment of compensation events is based entirely on their effect on the Time Charge and time. If some or all of the work arising from a compensation event has already been done, the Time Charge should be readily assessed from records. Forecasting future Time Charges is less straightforward. Estimates of resources and productivity rates are required. For Options C and E, the *Consultant* is paid for the compensation event on an actual time basis. However, the quotations are used for budgeting purposes in providing the forecasts under subclause 21.4 and in Option C for changing the total of the Prices to be used in calculating the *Consultant*'s share (clause 54).

63.2   The Prices can be reduced only when expressly permitted in the contract.

63.3   No compensation event can result in a reduction in the time for carrying out the *services*, i.e. an earlier Completion Date.

The first stage in assessing whether the Completion Date should be delayed as a result of a compensation event is to adjust the programme to take account of the compensation event with any appropriate adjustments to staff time risk allowances (subclause 63.6). Any float in the programme before planned Completion is available to mitigate or avoid any consequential delay to planned Completion. If planned Completion is delayed, the Completion Date is delayed by the same period. If planned Completion is not delayed, the Completion Date is not changed. The same rule applies to assessing the delay to a Key Date.

63.4   This subclause restricts the rights of the Parties in assessing the effects of a compensation event.

63.5 The *Consultant*'s duty to give an early warning is stated in subclause 15.1. The sanction if the *Consultant* fails to give early warning is stated in this subclause. It is possible that early warning could have allowed actions to be taken which would have reduced costs and saved time. It is important that the *Employer* notifies the *Consultant* of his decision that early warning should have been given (subclause 61.5) so that the *Consultant* knows the correct basis for his assessment.

63.6 Allowances for staff time risk must be included in forecasts of Time Charge and time. The value of the allowances is greater when the work is uncertain and there is high chance of a *Consultant*'s risk happening. It is least when the uncertainties are small.

63.7 This subclause protects the *Employer* against inefficiency on the part of the *Consultant*. The reference to changing the Accepted Programme is made so that it is clear that the *Consultant* is expected to alter his arrangements when necessary.

63.8 This subclause expresses the 'contra proferentem' rule, which interprets an ambiguity or inconsistency against the party responsible for drafting the document in which it occurs.

63.9 If the *Employer* instructs a change to the Scope, the Condition of the *Consultant*'s work to meet a Key Date (as described in the Contract Data) may be affected. The Condition may need to be changed.

63.10 It is possible that a compensation event may require some work to be done by a category of person which is not included in the list in Contract Data part two. In this subclause the *Consultant* is required to propose *staff rates* for such people.

63.11 The first of these deductions avoids the *Employer* having to pay for costs which the *Consultant* should have insured against. If the *Consultant* does not insure as required by the contract, such costs are at his own risk. The second deduction makes certain that the *Consultant* does not receive double payment as a result, for example, of insurance which he has voluntarily taken out or from insuring for a greater cover than required by the contract.

The *Employer*'s assessments 64

64.1 The four circumstances in which the *Employer* assesses a compensation event are stated. The first and third derive from some failure of the *Consultant* to fulfill an obligation under the contract. The second and fourth derive from the *Employer* not accepting a submission from the *Consultant*. The *Employer* is motivated to make a fair and reasonable assessment in the knowledge that the *Consultant* may refer the matter to the *Adjudicator* who may change the assessment.

64.2 This subclause states the circumstances in which the *Employer* is to use his own assessment of the programme for the remaining work in his assessment of a compensation event. This is a major incentive for the *Consultant* to keep his programme up to date.

64.3 This subclause allows the *Employer* the same time to make his assessment as the *Consultant* was allowed for his.

64.4 The procedure in this subclause is designed to deal with a situation where the *Employer* does not assess a compensation event within the time stated in this contract or a longer agreed time. The *Consultant* may notify the *Employer* accordingly, which effectively provides the *Employer* with a two week 'period of grace' to respond. If this produces no action from the *Employer*, the quotation submitted by the *Consultant* is treated as having been accepted.

Implementing **65**
compensation events 65.1   This subclause should be read in conjunction with subclause 65.3 for Options A and C, with subclause 65.4 for Option E and with subclause 65.5 for Option G.

   Implementation is achieved by the *Employer* changing the Prices and the Completion Date and the Key Dates in accordance with the assessment, of which he has notified the *Consultant*. In the case of Option G, changes to the final total of the Prices and the programme for a Task are also included.

65.2   This subclause emphasises the finality of the assessment of compensation events. If the records of resources on work actually carried out show that actual Time Charge and timing are different from the forecasts included in the accepted quotation or in the *Employer*'s assessment, the assessment is not changed. The only circumstances in which a review is possible are those stated in subclause 61.5.

7 Rights to material

CORE CLAUSES

The Parties' use of material **70**

70.1   Under this subclause, the *Consultant* retains rights over material provided by him, but the *Employer* may use it for the purposes stated in the Scope. If Option X9 is used, the effect is to transfer these rights to the *Employer*, with any exceptions being stated in the Scope. The subclause is drafted in general terms and may not involve such rights as designers' copyright. The *Consultant* may reasonably insist that any re-use of material which he provides is entirely at the *Employer*'s risk, unless the *Employer* obtains prior verification by the *Consultant*. The *Consultant* may further seek indemnity from the *Consultant* against claims arising from such re-use. This emphasises the importance of the drafting of the Scope, to make clear liabilities for use or re-use by the *Employer* of material produced by the *Consultant*. In England and Wales, legal recognition of the right to use material or of the transfer of its ownership can only be achieved if stamped documentary evidence is provided and Stamp Duty is paid.

70.2   The *Consultant* may use any material provided by the *Employer*, but this is restricted to the extent necessary to Provide the Services.

70.3   Confidentiality is achieved by the provisions of this subclause. The *Consultant* may, however, publicise certain information, provided he obtains the *Employer*'s agreement under subclause 71.1.

70.4   The *Consultant* may use material produced under this contract for other work. Exceptions are stated in the Scope.

8 Indemnity, insurance and liability

CORE CLAUSES

Indemnity **80**

80.1 This subclause protects the *Employer* in the event that the *Consultant* infringes the rights of Others who may seek redress from the *Employer*. 'Others' are defined in subclause 11.2(7). The only exception is when the *Employer* himself provides things for the *Consultant*'s use.

Insurance cover **81**

81.1 Three main types of insurance are required.

(a) Professional indemnity insurance

This is the first insurance stated in the Insurance Table, and provides an indemnity in respect of any sum which the *Consultant* may become legally liable to pay arising out of claims made against him during the period of insurance as a result of any neglect, error or omission in carrying out his professional activities.

The amount of cover is to be stated in the Contract Data. In some circumstances, some insurers insist on a maximum sum for any one claim and in the aggregate on the period of insurance.

The period for which insurance cover is required is also to be stated in the Contract Data. Claims in respect of professional indemnity insurance normally have to be made during the period of insurance. Claims cannot normally be made after the period of insurance even though the act of neglect may have taken place during the period of insurance. Thus, in dealing with the period of cover, it is desirable that the policy is kept in force after completion of the services to deal with claims made in respect of negligent acts which do not manifest themselves until some time after. To provide adequate cover in these circumstances, the period stated should be the relevant legal limitation period after Completion.

(b) Public liability insurance

This is the second insurance in the Insurance Table and indemnifies the *Consultant* against his legal liability for damages arising from bodily injury to or death of a person (other than the *Consultant*'s employees) or loss of or damage to third party property occurring during the period of insurance. In this type of insurance, the act of neglect leading to liability has to take place during the currency of the policy, but claims can be made afterwards. Hence there is no need to maintain the policy after Completion.

(c) Employer's liability insurance

The third insurance in the Insurance Table provides indemnity for legal liability for bodily injury to or death of the *Consultant*'s employees arising out of or in the course of their employment. This insurance is compulsory in the United Kingdom, the statutory provisions requiring insurance for a minimum of £2 million for each occurrence. Elsewhere in the world other regulations may apply, requiring workmen's compensation-type coverage or participation in state social security schemes. Insurance cover may terminate on Completion.

If the *Employer* provides property for the use of the *Consultant* in providing the *services*, he may require the *Consultant* to insure it for the period during which it is being used by the *Consultant*. Any such requirements should be stated in the Contract Data, with cover being for the replacement value of the property.

In some circumstances it may be more appropriate and convenient for the *Employer* to effect some of the *Consultant*'s insurances, for example by taking out a project insurance policy covering contractors and consultants. In addition, it is likely that other consultants and contractors will be required to carry their own insurances covering certain risks. Where these are relevant to the risks taken by the *Consultant* under this contract, they should be listed in the Contract Data. Examples are contractor's works and third party liability insurances and the *Employer*'s own building insurances.

81.2 Insurers and brokers will generally not release copies of consultants' insurance policies. It is normal, however, for the *Consultant* to provide a certificate from his broker confirming that he does hold the insurances. In the same way, the *Employer* is required to provide a certificate on request confirming that he holds the necessary insurances.

Limit of liability 82

82.1 The *Consultant*'s total liability to the *Employer* (i.e. the maximum the *Employer* could recover for the *Consultant*'s negligence) will be the amount stated in the Contract Data. This will normally be the amount of the insurance cover. When setting any limit higher than the insurance cover, the consequences on the work of the *Consultant* will need to be recognised (see Contract Data under 'Optional statements'). The *Consultant*'s total liability is fully described, and excludes five matters. Further limitations of the *Consultant*'s liability may be introduced by incorporating Option X18.

82.2 If the *Consultant* is found to be legally liable along with others, the *Consultant*'s liability to the *Employer* is limited to his proportionate failure. If, for example, a court were to conclude that a supervisor appointed as a *Consultant* under the PSC to supervise a construction contract was 15% liable and the contractor 85% liable for the *Employer*'s losses, the maximum the *Employer* could recover from the *Consultant* would be 15% of his losses up to the limit of insurance or other figure stated.

9 Termination

This section describes the circumstances under which the Parties may terminate the *Consultant*'s appointment and the subsequent procedures.

Termination **90**

90.1 to 90.3 Both the *Employer* and the *Consultant* have limited rights of termination of appointment of the *Consultant* under the core clauses. The *Employer* effectively may terminate whenever he no longer requires the *services*. He may also terminate if a *Consultant* is substantially in breach of contract. The *Consultant* may terminate if a payment has not been made within eight weeks after serving a notice that payment is overdue.

In any event either Party may terminate on the insolvency of the other. The terms used in subclause 90.1 for insolvency are those current in English law, but the subclause allows for their equivalent in other jurisdictions.

Secondary Option X11 provides for termination at will by the *Employer* (see guidance note on Option X11). There is no equivalent right for the *Consultant*.

90.4 The event described is commonly known as 'force majeure' in certain jurisdictions. The subclause entitles the *Employer* to terminate if the event prevents the *Consultant* from completing the *services* or delaying Completion by thirteen weeks or more.

Procedures on termination **91**

91.1 This subclause covers the work required following termination to achieve an orderly close-down of the *Consultant*'s *services*. It includes for the assignment of a subconsultancy, but it should be recognised that the co-operation of the Subconsultant would be required to complete the *services* satisfactorily.

It is possible that in certain circumstances material provided by the *Consultant* is later revised by the *Employer* for purposes which are not appropriate but over which the *Consultant* has no control. If such circumstances are likely to occur, liability of the Parties should be made clear in the contract.

After termination, the *Consultant* must hand over to the *Employer* all material he was preparing for him under the contract, but the *Consultant* is entitled to keep the material until he has been paid. Any dispute over the amount of the final payment would be subject to adjudication.

Payment on termination **92**

92.1 92.2 These subclauses set out how the final payment from the *Employer* to the *Consultant* is assessed following termination. The *Consultant* is paid the amount he was already due plus any other costs to which he is committed. If the termination is due to the insolvency or default of the *Consultant*, the *Employer* is entitled to deduct from those costs the forecast additional cost to him of completing the *services*. This would include the costs of appointing a replacement consultant.

MAIN OPTION CLAUSES

Option C: Target contract

Payment on termination **92**

92.3 Following termination of an Option C target contract, the *Consultant*'s share is assessed at that time in accordance with clause 54 using the Price for Services Provided to Date at termination and the total of the Prices for the work done as set out in the Activity Schedule.

Flow charts for the

Professional Services Contract

FLOW CHARTS

PREFACE

These flow charts depict the procedures followed when using the NEC3 Professional Services Contract (PSC). They are intended to help people using the PSC to see how the various PSC core clauses and Options come together to produce clear and precise sequences of action for the people involved.

The flow charts are not part of any contract. Much of the text and many of the words taken from the PSC itself are abbreviated in the flow charts. The flow charts depict almost all of the sequences of action set out in the PSC. Many of the sequences interact, and because of this, users of the flow charts will often have to review more than one sheet in order to track the full sequence of actions in one area.

ABBREVIATIONS USED IN THE FLOW CHART BOXES

FC 61	Flow chart for clause 61
FC X5	Flow chart for secondary Option X5
E	*Employer*
C	*Consultant*
SC	Subconsultant
CD	Contract Data
CE	Compensation event
PAF	Price Adjustment Factor

Legend

CHART START

HEADINGS
Headings in caps
provide guidance

STATEMENTS
If a subclause is
referenced, text
is from the NEC

LOGIC LINKS
Links go to right
and/or downward
unless shown

QUESTION
Answer question
to determine the
route to follow

SUBROUTINE
Include another
flow chart here

CONTINUATION
Link to matching
point(s) on other
chart sheets

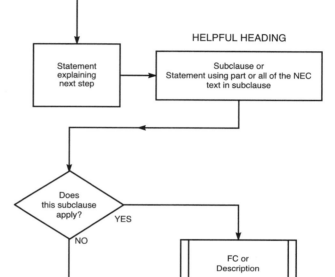

CHART TITLE
Chart number,
title and sheet

**Flow chart or Sheet 1 of 2
Description**

CONTINUATION

CHART FINISH

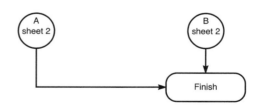

CHART TITLE

**Flow chart or Sheet 2 of 2
Description**

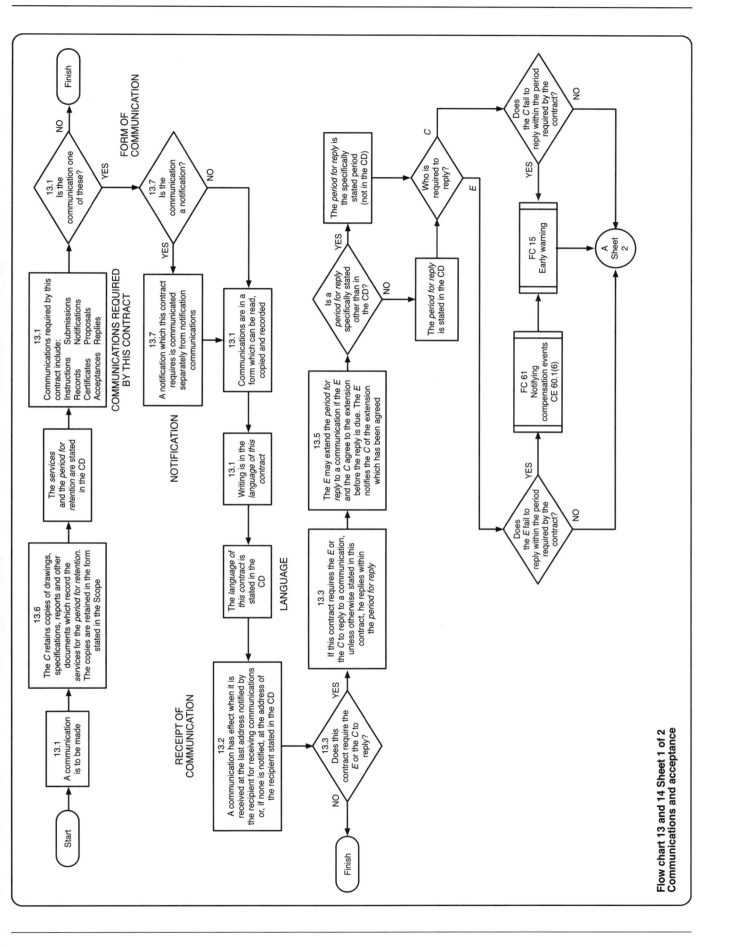

Flow chart 13 and 14 Sheet 1 of 2
Communications and acceptance

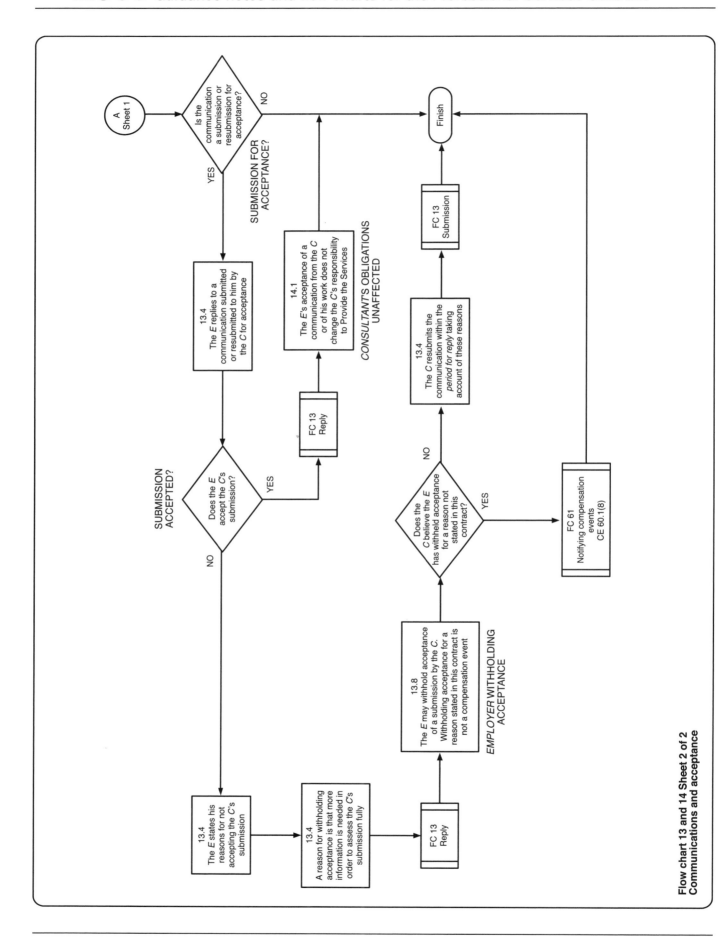

A Sheet 1

Is the communication a submission or resubmission for acceptance?

SUBMISSION FOR ACCEPTANCE?

YES → NO → Finish

13.4
The E replies to a communication submitted or resubmitted to him by the C for acceptance

14.1
The E's acceptance of a communication from the C or of his work does not change the C's responsibility to Provide the Services

CONSULTANT'S OBLIGATIONS UNAFFECTED

FC 13 Submission

SUBMISSION ACCEPTED?

Does the E accept the C's submission?

NO

YES

FC 13 Reply

13.4
The C resubmits the communication within the *period for reply* taking account of these reasons

NO

Does the C believe the E has withheld acceptance for a reason not stated in this contract?

YES

FC 61 Notifying compensation events CE 60.1(8)

13.4
The E states his reasons for not accepting the C's submission

13.4
A reason for withholding acceptance is that more information is needed in order to assess the C's submission fully

FC 13 Reply

13.8
The E may withhold acceptance of a submission by the C. Withholding acceptance for a reason stated in this contract is not a compensation event

EMPLOYER WITHHOLDING ACCEPTANCE

Flow chart 13 and 14 Sheet 2 of 2
Communications and acceptance

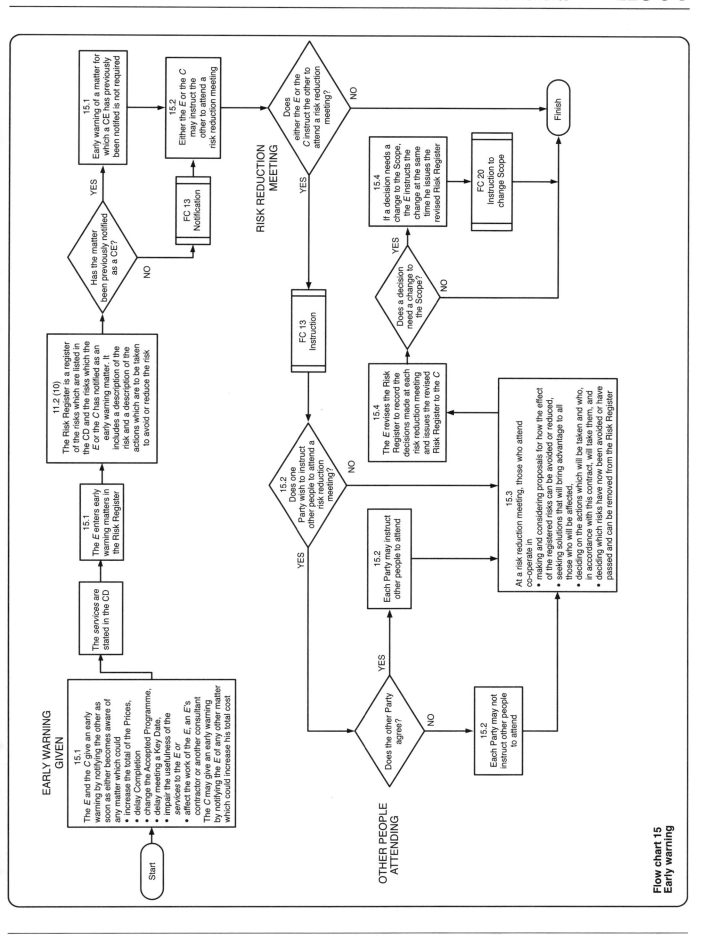

EARLY WARNING GIVEN

Start

15.1
The E and the C give an early warning by notifying the other as soon as either becomes aware of any matter which could
• increase the total of the Prices,
• delay Completion
• change the Accepted Programme,
• delay meeting a Key Date,
• impair the usefulness of the services to the E or
• affect the work of the E, an E's contractor or another consultant
The C may give an early warning by notifying the E of any other matter which could increase his total cost

The services are stated in the CD

15.1
The E enters early warning matters in the Risk Register

11.2 (10)
The Risk Register is a register of the risks which are listed in the CD and the risks which the E or the C has notified as an early warning matter. It includes a description of the risk and a description of the actions which are to be taken to avoid or reduce the risk

Has the matter been previously notified as a CE?

NO → FC 13 Notification

YES → 15.1 Early warning of a matter for which a CE has previously been notified is not required

15.2
Either the E or the C may instruct the other to attend a risk reduction meeting

RISK REDUCTION MEETING

Does either the E or the C instruct the other to attend a risk reduction meeting?

NO → Finish

YES → FC 13 Instruction

15.2
Does one Party wish to instruct other people to attend a risk reduction meeting?

YES →

NO → 15.4
The E revises the Risk Register to record the decisions made at each risk reduction meeting and issues the revised Risk Register to the C

Does a decision need a change to the Scope?

YES → 15.4
If a decision needs a change to the Scope, the E instructs the change at the same time he issues the revised Risk Register

→ FC 20 Instruction to change Scope → Finish

NO →

OTHER PEOPLE ATTENDING

Does the other Party agree?

YES → 15.2 Each Party may instruct other people to attend

NO → 15.2 Each Party may not instruct other people to attend

15.3
At a risk reduction meeting, those who attend co-operate in
• making and considering proposals for how the effect of the registered risks can be avoided or reduced,
• seeking solutions that will bring advantage to all those who will be affected,
• deciding on the actions which will be taken and who, in accordance with this contract, will take them, and
• deciding which risks have now been avoided or have passed and can be removed from the Risk Register

Flow chart 15
Early warning

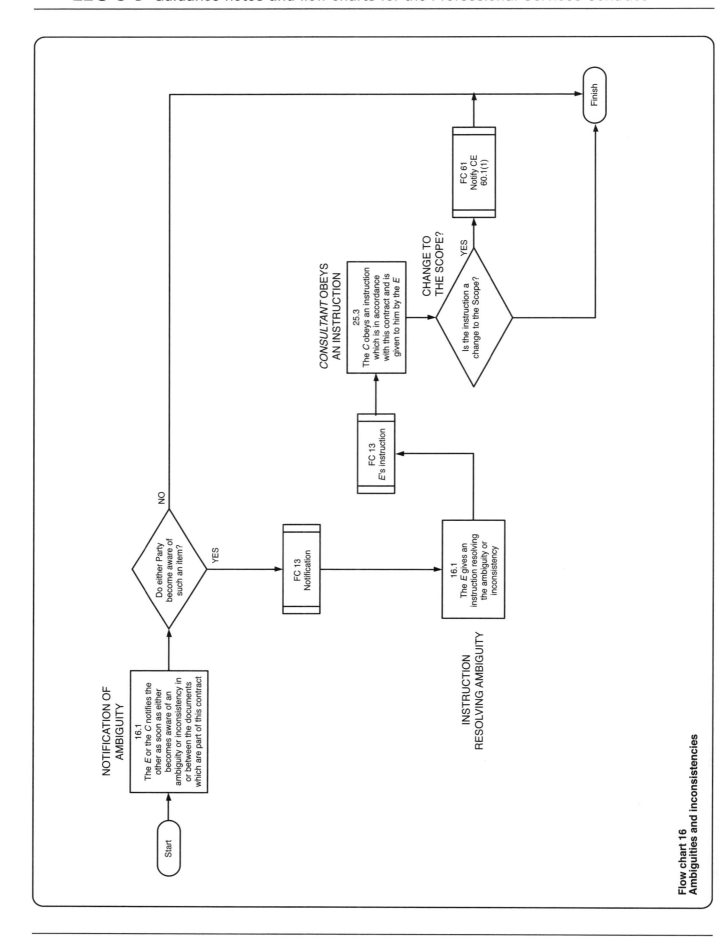

Flow chart 16
Ambiguities and inconsistencies

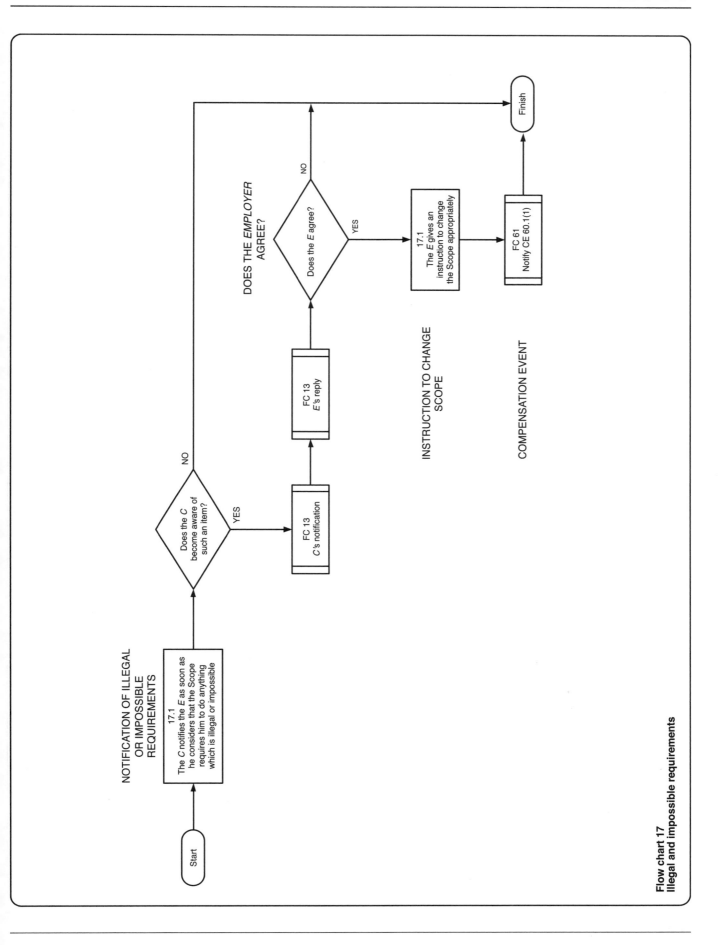

NOTIFICATION OF ILLEGAL OR IMPOSSIBLE REQUIREMENTS

Start

17.1
The C notifies the E as soon as he considers that the Scope requires him to do anything which is illegal or impossible

Does the C become aware of such an item?

NO

YES

FC 13
C's notification

FC 13
E's reply

DOES THE EMPLOYER AGREE?

Does the E agree?

NO

YES

INSTRUCTION TO CHANGE SCOPE

17.1
The E gives an instruction to change the Scope appropriately

COMPENSATION EVENT

FC 61
Notify CE 60.1(1)

Finish

Flow chart 17
Illegal and impossible requirements

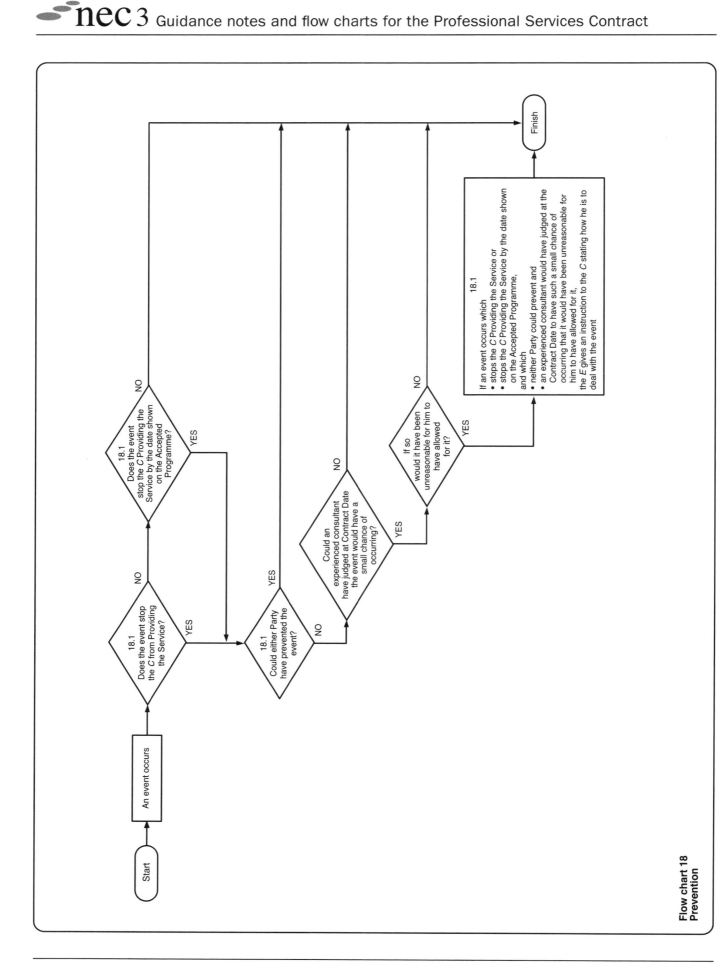

Start

An event occurs

18.1
Does the event stop the C from Providing the Service?

18.1
Does the event stop the C Providing the Service by the date shown on the Accepted Programme?

NO

YES

NO

YES

18.1
Could either Party have prevented the event?

YES

NO

Could an experienced consultant have judged at Contract Date the event would have a small chance of occurring?

NO

YES

If so would it have been unreasonable for him to have allowed for it?

NO

YES

18.1

If an event occurs which
• stops the C Providing the Service or
• stops the C Providing the Service by the date shown on the Accepted Programme,
and which
• neither Party could prevent and
• an experienced consultant would have judged at the Contract Date to have such a small chance of occurring that it would have been unreasonable for him to have allowed for it,
the E gives an instruction to the C stating how he is to deal with the event

Finish

**Flow chart 18
Prevention**

www.neccontract.com

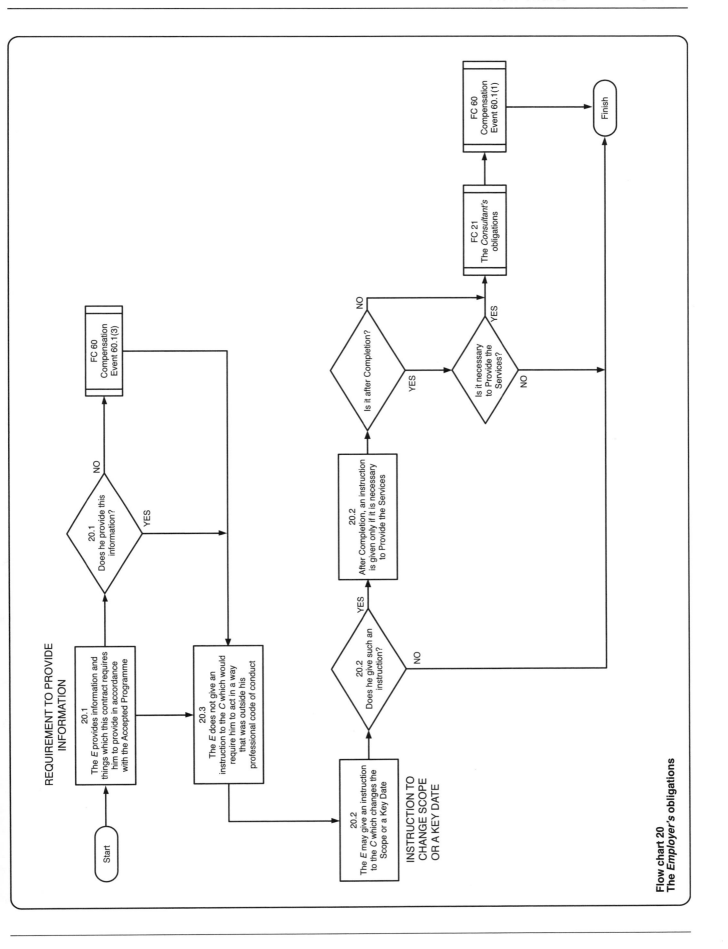

REQUIREMENT TO PROVIDE INFORMATION

20.1
The *E* provides information and things which this contract requires him to provide in accordance with the Accepted Programme

20.1
Does he provide this information?

NO → FC 60 Compensation Event 60.1(3)

YES →

20.3
The *E* does not give an instruction to the *C* which would require him to act in a way that was outside his professional code of conduct

INSTRUCTION TO CHANGE SCOPE OR A KEY DATE

20.2
The *E* may give an instruction to the *C* which changes the Scope or a Key Date

20.2
Does he give such an instruction?

YES →

20.2
After Completion, an instruction is given only if it is necessary to Provide the Services

Is it after Completion?

NO → FC 21 The *Consultant's* obligations → FC 60 Compensation Event 60.1(1) → Finish

YES →

Is it necessary to Provide the Services?

YES ↑

NO →

20.2
Does he give such an instruction? — NO →

Start

Flow chart 20
The *Employer's* obligations

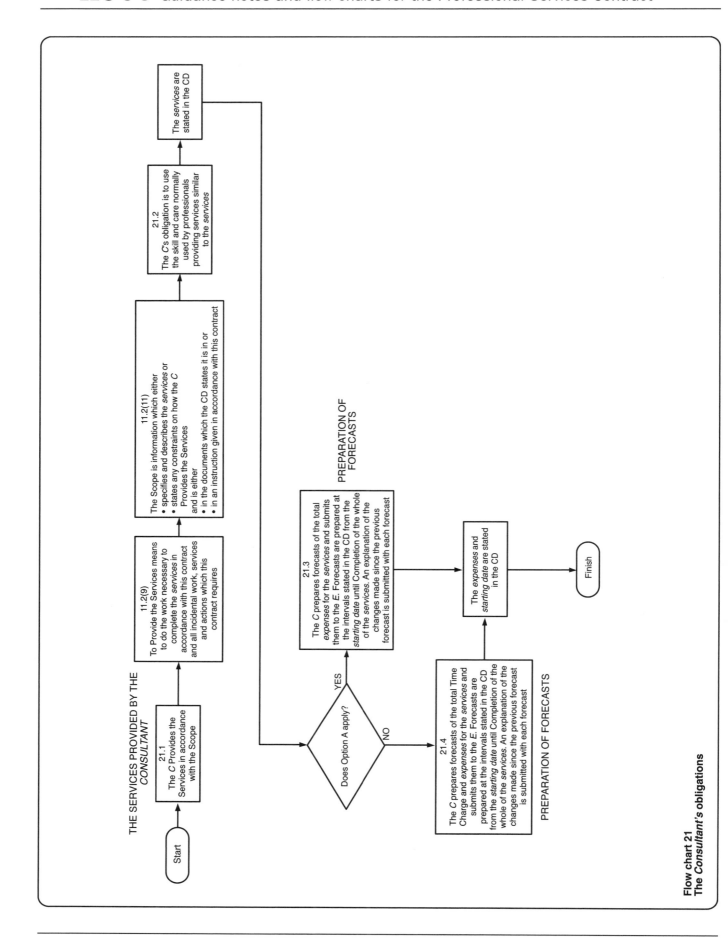

THE SERVICES PROVIDED BY THE CONSULTANT

Start

21.1
The C Provides the Services in accordance with the Scope

11.2(9)
To Provide the Services means to do the work necessary to complete the *services* in accordance with this contract and all incidental work, services and actions which this contract requires

11.2(11)
The Scope is information which either
• specifies and describes the *services* or
• states any constraints on how the C Provides the Services
and is either
• in the documents which the CD states it is in or
• in an instruction given in accordance with this contract

21.2
The C's obligation is to use the skill and care normally used by professionals providing services similar to the *services*

The *services* are stated in the CD

PREPARATION OF FORECASTS

Does Option A apply?

YES

21.3
The C prepares forecasts of the total *expenses* for the *services* and submits them to the E. Forecasts are prepared at the intervals stated in the CD from the *starting date* until Completion of the whole of the *services*. An explanation of the changes made since the previous forecast is submitted with each forecast

NO

21.4
The C prepares forecasts of the total Time Charge and *expenses* for the *services* and submits them to the E. Forecasts are prepared at the intervals stated in the CD from the *starting date* until Completion of the whole of the *services*. An explanation of the changes made since the previous forecast is submitted with each forecast

PREPARATION OF FORECASTS

The *expenses* and *starting date* are stated in the CD

Finish

Flow chart 21
The *Consultant's* obligations

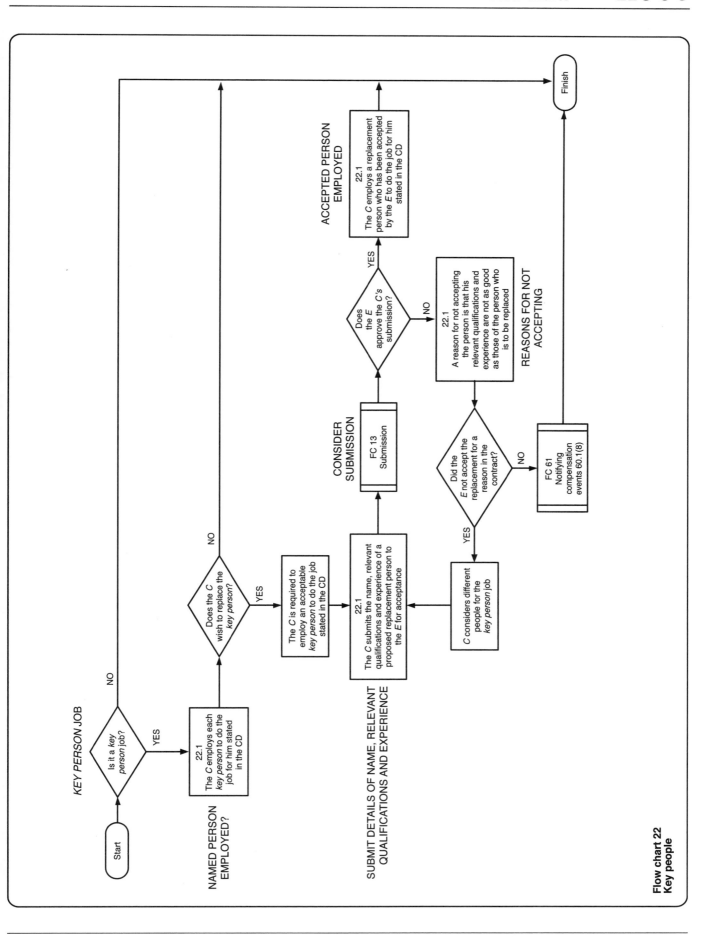

**Flow chart 22
Key people**

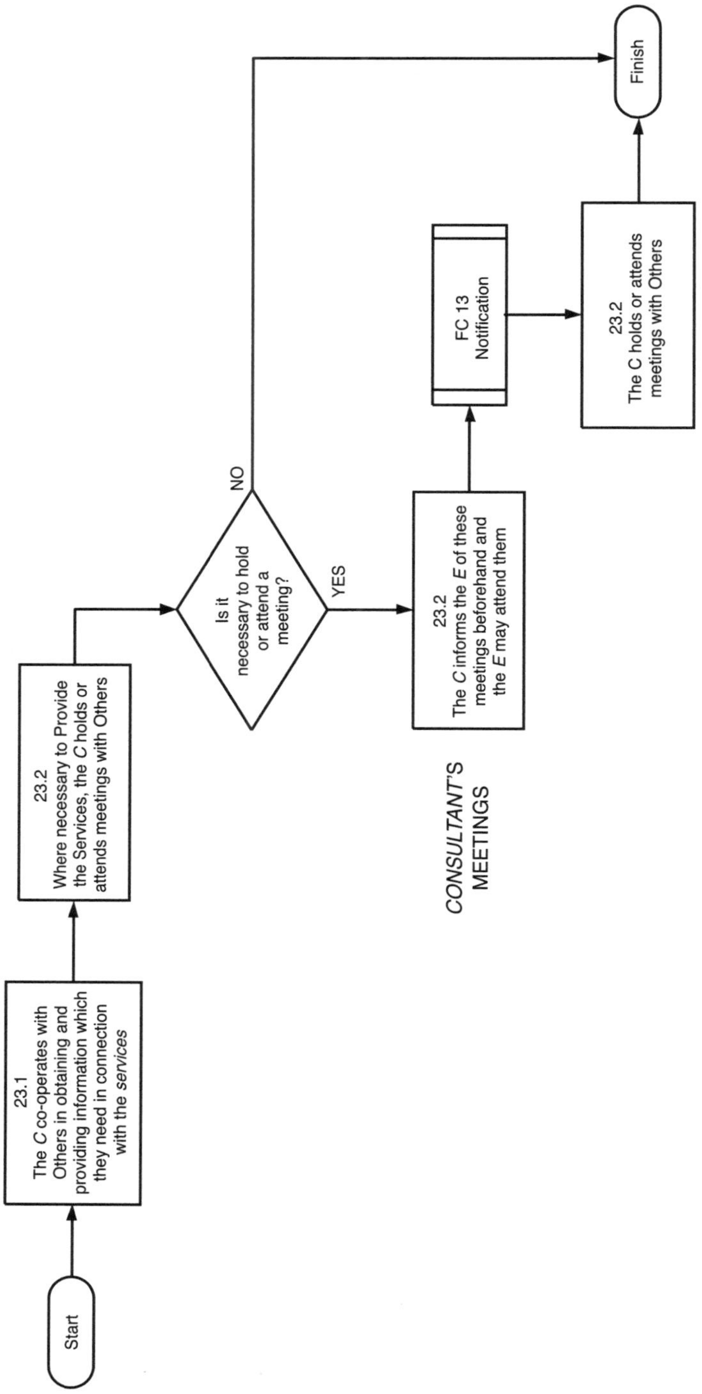
Start
23.1
The *C* co-operates with Others in obtaining and providing information which they need in connection with the *services*
23.2
Where necessary to Provide the Services, the *C* holds or attends meetings with Others
Is it necessary to hold or attend a meeting?
NO
YES
23.2
The *C* informs the *E* of these meetings beforehand and the *E* may attend them
CONSULTANT'S MEETINGS
FC 13
Notification
23.2
The C holds or attends meetings with Others
Finish

Flow chart 23
Working with the *Employer* and Others

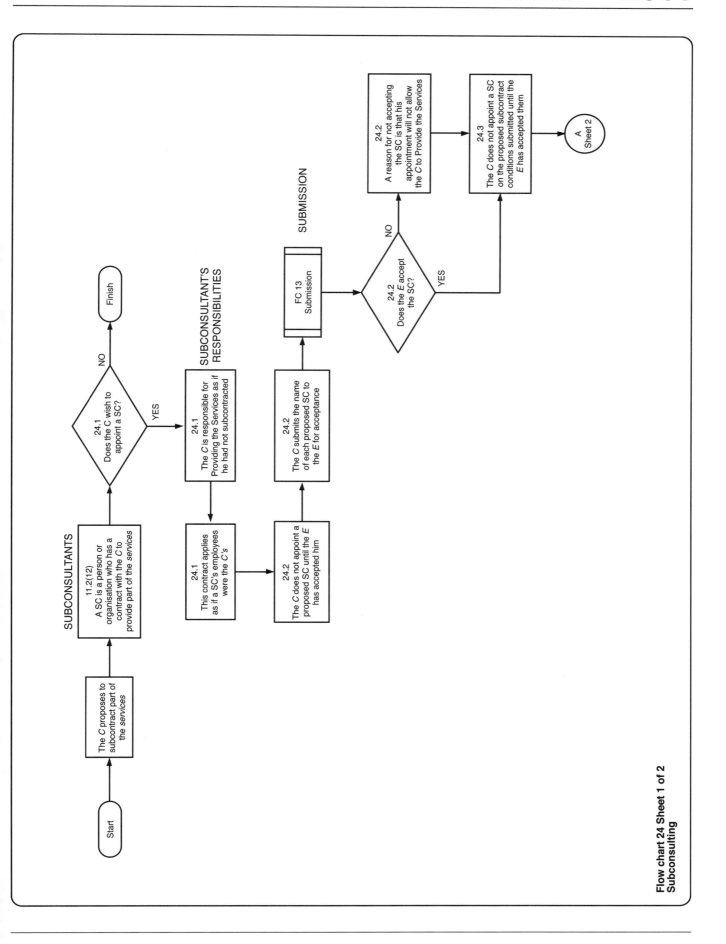

SUBCONSULTANTS

Start

The *C* proposes to subcontract part of the *services*

11.2(12)
A SC is a person or organisation who has a contract with the *C* to provide part of the *services*

24.1
Does the *C* wish to appoint a SC?

NO — Finish

YES

SUBCONSULTANT'S RESPONSIBILITIES

24.1
The *C* is responsible for Providing the Services as if he had not subcontracted

24.1
This contract applies as if a SC's employees were the *C's*

24.2
The *C* does not appoint a proposed SC until the *E* has accepted him

24.2
The *C* submits the name of each proposed SC to the *E* for acceptance

SUBMISSION

FC 13
Submission

24.2
Does the *E* accept the SC?

NO

YES

24.2
A reason for not accepting the SC is that his appointment will not allow the *C* to Provide the Services

24.3
The *C* does not appoint a SC on the proposed subcontract conditions submitted until the *E* has accepted them

A
Sheet 2

Flow chart 24 Sheet 1 of 2
Subconsulting

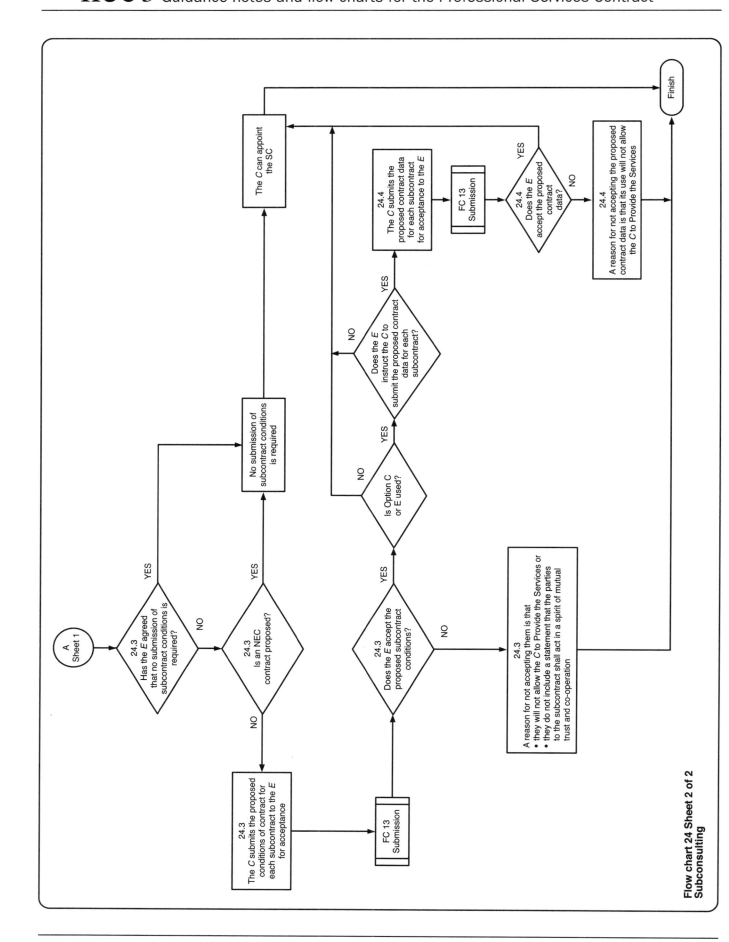

Flow chart 24 Sheet 2 of 2
Subconsulting

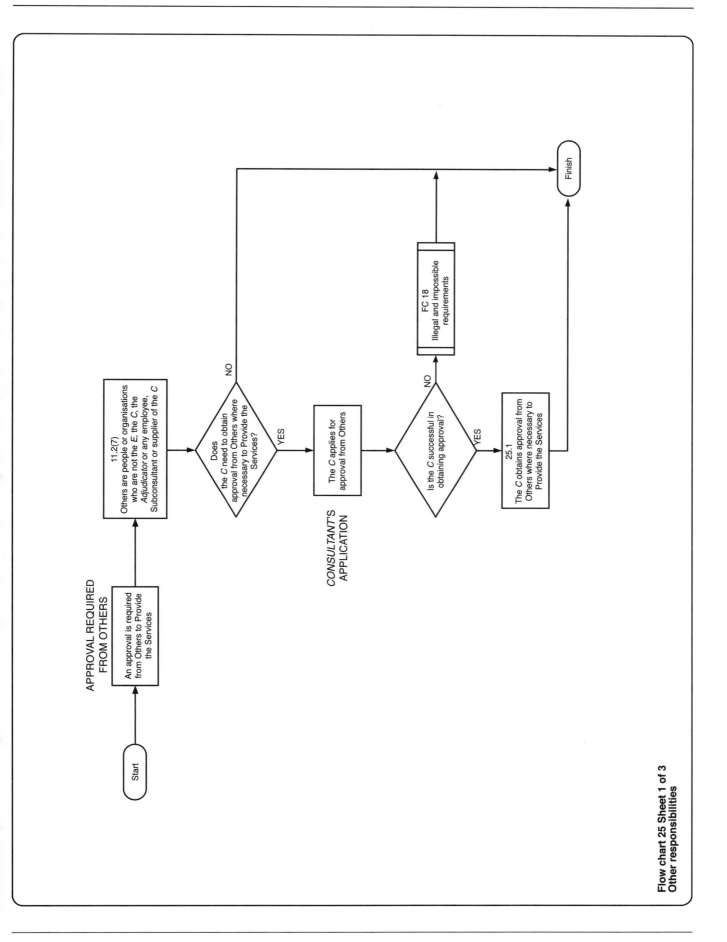

APPROVAL REQUIRED FROM OTHERS

Start

An approval is required from Others to Provide the Services

11.2(7)
Others are people or organisations who are not the *E*, the *C*, the *Adjudicator* or any employee, Subconsultant or supplier of the *C*

Does the *C* need to obtain approval from Others where necessary to Provide the Services?

NO

YES

CONSULTANT'S APPLICATION

The *C* applies for approval from Others

Is the *C* successful in obtaining approval?

NO

YES

FC 18
Illegal and impossible requirements

25.1
The *C* obtains approval from Others where necessary to Provide the Services

Finish

Flow chart 25 Sheet 1 of 3
Other responsibilities

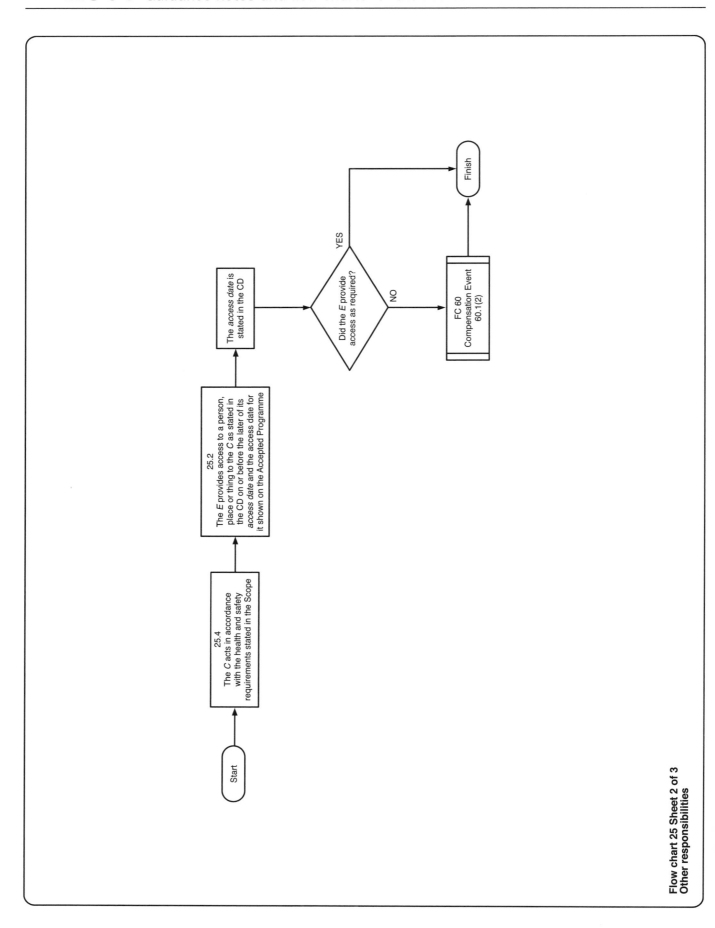

Start

25.4
The C acts in accordance with the health and safety requirements stated in the Scope

25.2
The E provides access to a person, place or thing to the C as stated in the CD on or before the later of its *access date* and the access date for it shown on the Accepted Programme

The *access date* is stated in the CD

Did the E provide access as required?

YES → Finish

NO → FC 60 Compensation Event 60.1(2) → Finish

Flow chart 25 Sheet 2 of 3
Other responsibilities

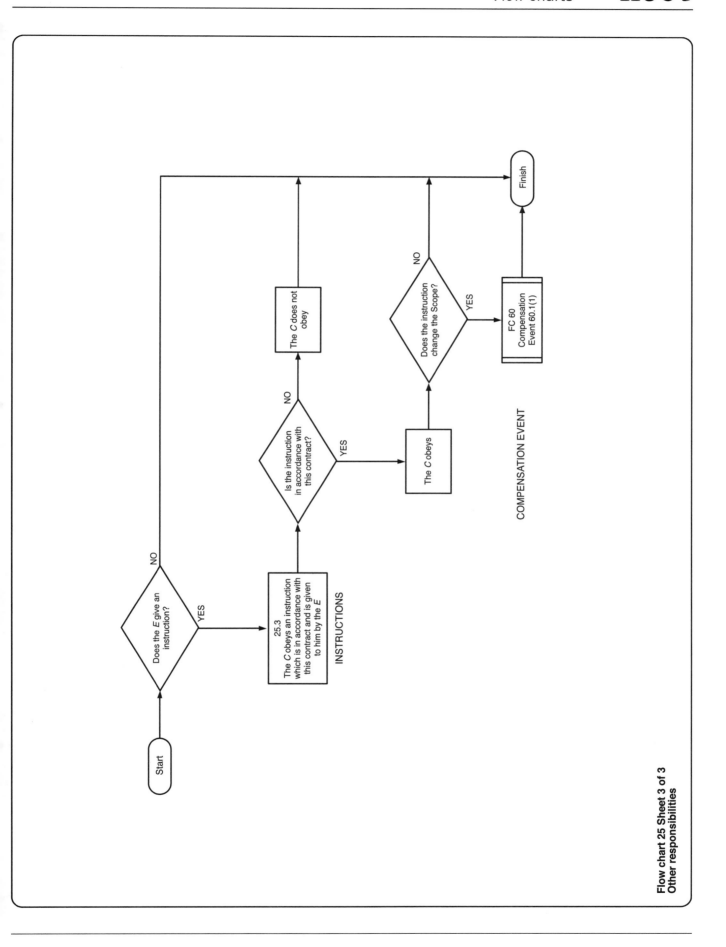

Start

Does the E give an instruction?

NO

YES

25.3
The C obeys an instruction which is in accordance with this contract and is given to him by the E

INSTRUCTIONS

Is the instruction in accordance with this contract?

NO

YES

The C does not obey

The C obeys

Does the instruction change the Scope?

NO

YES

Finish

FC 60
Compensation Event 60.1(1)

COMPENSATION EVENT

Flow chart 25 Sheet 3 of 3
Other responsibilities

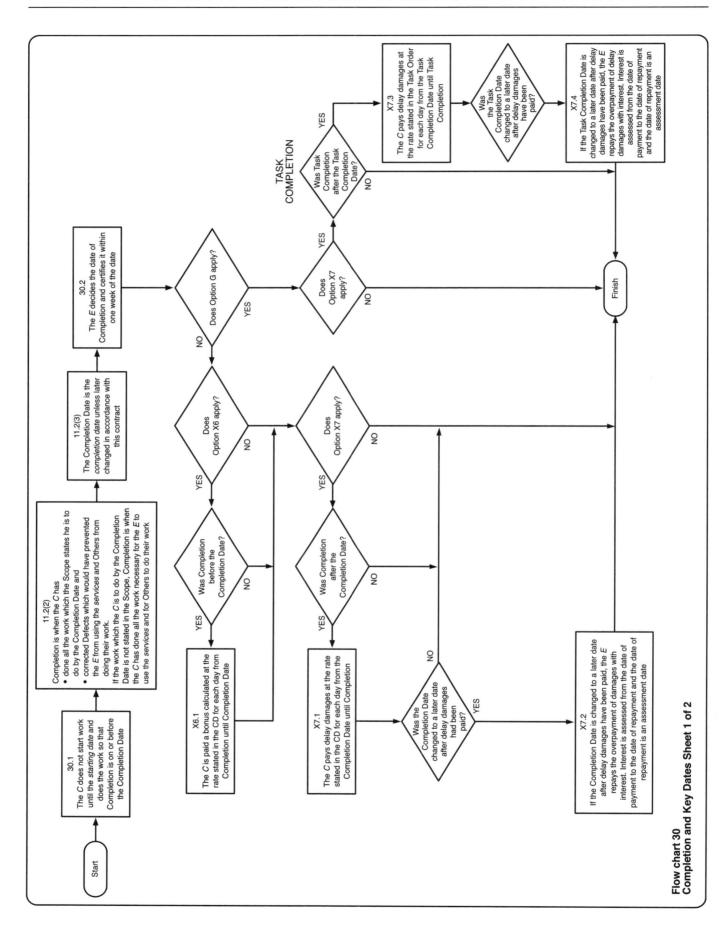

Flow chart 30
Completion and Key Dates Sheet 1 of 2

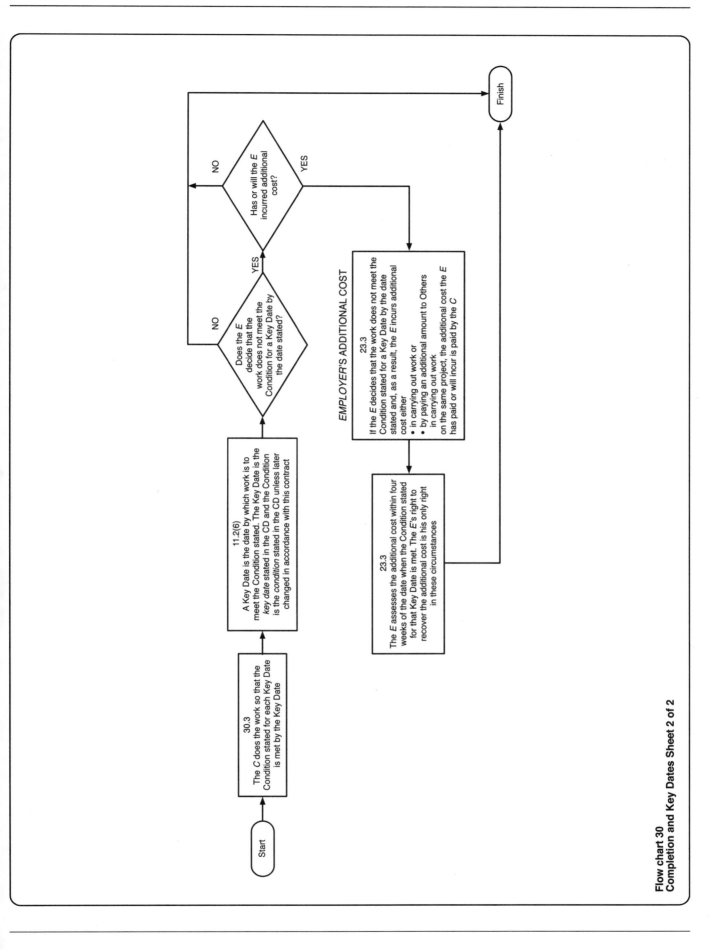

Start

30.3
The *C* does the work so that the Condition stated for each Key Date is met by the Key Date

11.2(6)
A Key Date is the date by which work is to meet the Condition stated. The Key Date is the *key date* stated in the CD and the Condition is the *condition* stated in the CD unless later changed in accordance with this contract

Does the *E* decide that the work does not meet the Condition for a Key Date by the date stated?

NO

YES

Has or will the *E* incurred additional cost?

NO → Finish

YES

EMPLOYER'S ADDITIONAL COST

23.3
If the *E* decides that the work does not meet the Condition stated for a Key Date by the date stated and, as a result, the *E* incurs additional cost either
• in carrying out work or
• by paying an additional amount to Others in carrying out work
on the same project, the additional cost the *E* has paid or will incur is paid by the *C*

23.3
The *E* assesses the additional cost within four weeks of the date when the Condition stated for that Key Date is met. The *E*'s right to recover the additional cost is his only right in these circumstances

Flow chart 30
Completion and Key Dates Sheet 2 of 2

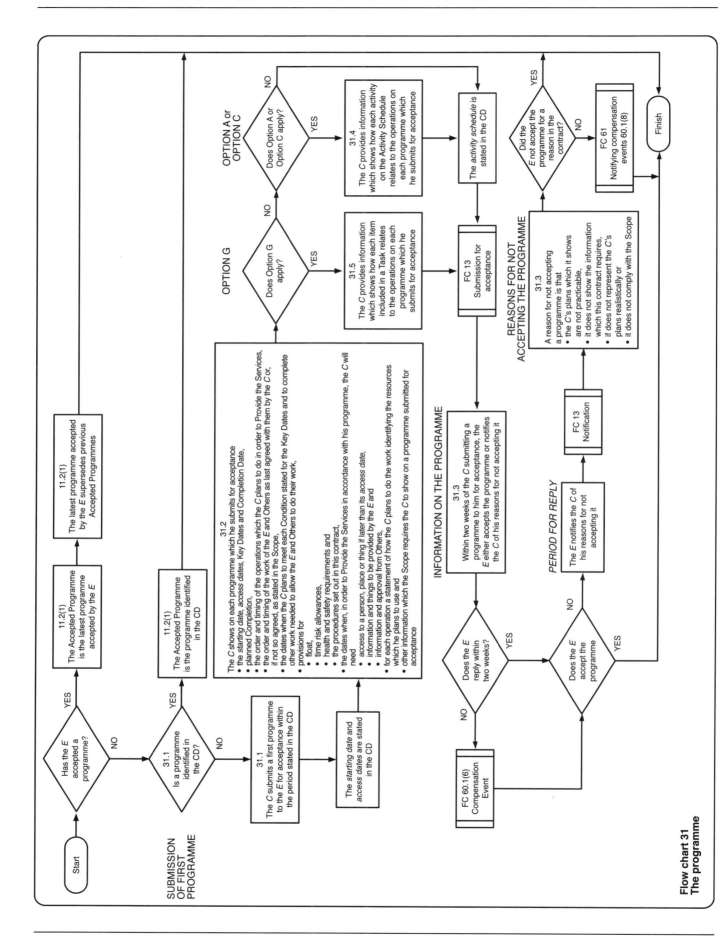

Flow chart 31
The programme

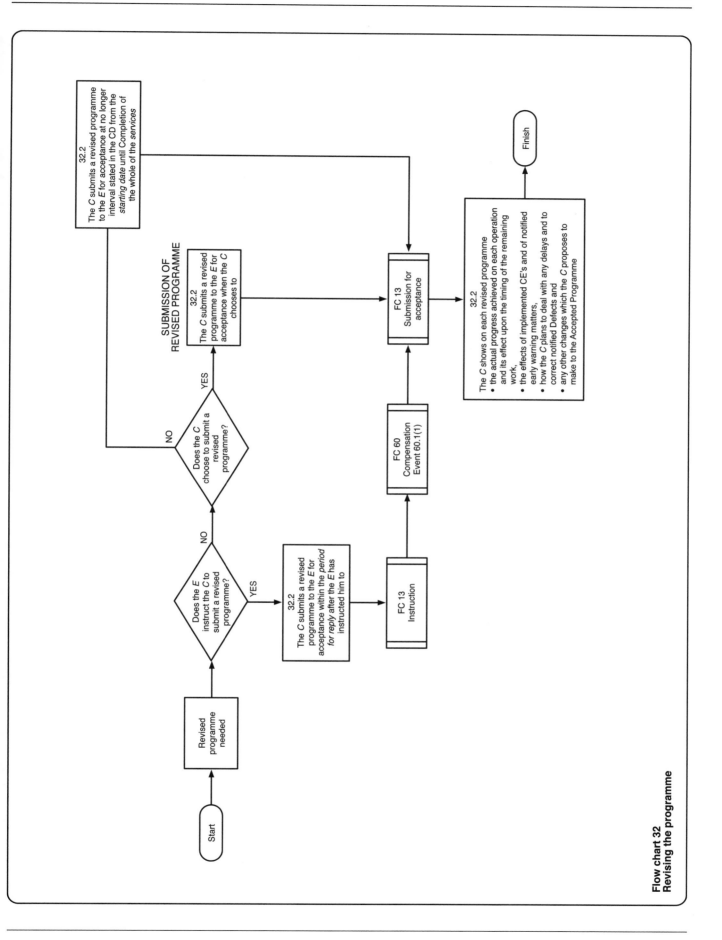

Start

Revised programme needed

Does the E instruct the C to submit a revised programme?

NO

YES

32.2
The C submits a revised programme to the E for acceptance within the *period for reply* after the E has instructed him to

FC 13
Instruction

FC 60
Compensation Event 60.1(1)

FC 13
Submission for acceptance

Does the C choose to submit a revised programme?

NO

YES

SUBMISSION OF REVISED PROGRAMME

32.2
The C submits a revised programme to the E for acceptance when the C chooses to

32.2
The C submits a revised programme to the E for acceptance at no longer interval stated in the CD from the *starting date* until Completion of the whole of the *services*

32.2
The C shows on each revised programme
• the actual progress achieved on each operation and its effect upon the timing of the remaining work,
• the effects of implemented CE's and of notified early warning matters,
• how the C plans to deal with any delays and to correct notified Defects and
• any other changes which the C proposes to make to the Accepted Programme

Finish

Flow chart 32
Revising the programme

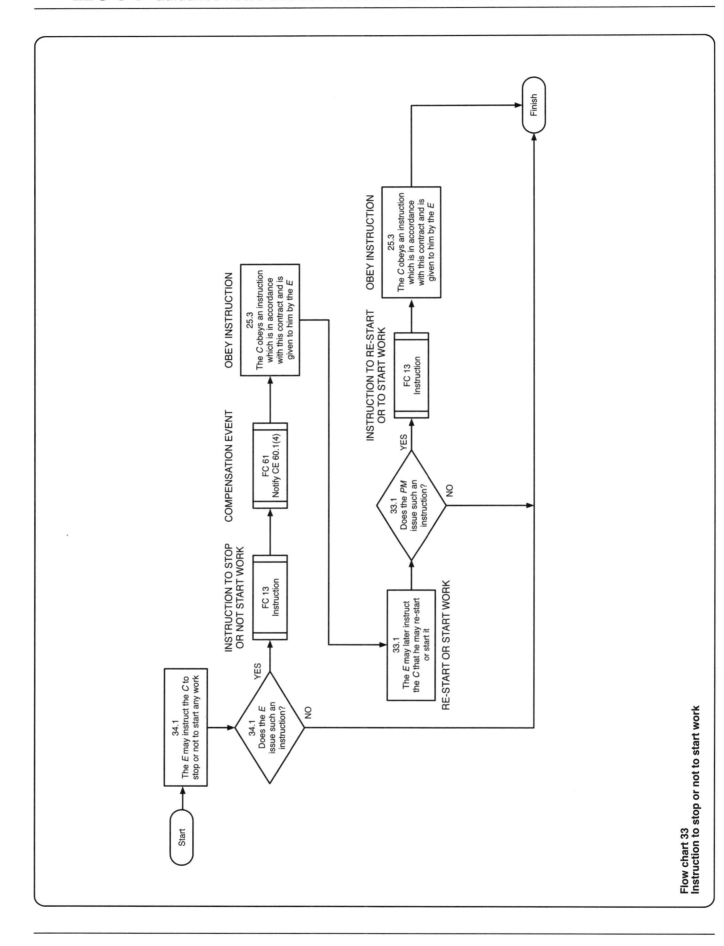

Start

INSTRUCTION TO STOP
OR NOT START WORK

34.1
The *E* may instruct the *C* to
stop or not to start any work

34.1
Does the *E*
issue such an
instruction?

YES

NO

FC 13
Instruction

COMPENSATION EVENT

FC 61
Notify CE 60.1(4)

OBEY INSTRUCTION

25.3
The *C* obeys an instruction
which is in accordance
with this contract and is
given to him by the *E*

RE-START OR START WORK

33.1
The *E* may later instruct
the *C* that he may re-start
or start it

33.1
Does the *PM*
issue such an
instruction?

YES

NO

INSTRUCTION TO RE-START
OR TO START WORK

FC 13
Instruction

OBEY INSTRUCTION

25.3
The *C* obeys an instruction
which is in accordance
with this contract and is
given to him by the *E*

Finish

Flow chart 33
Instruction to stop or not to start work

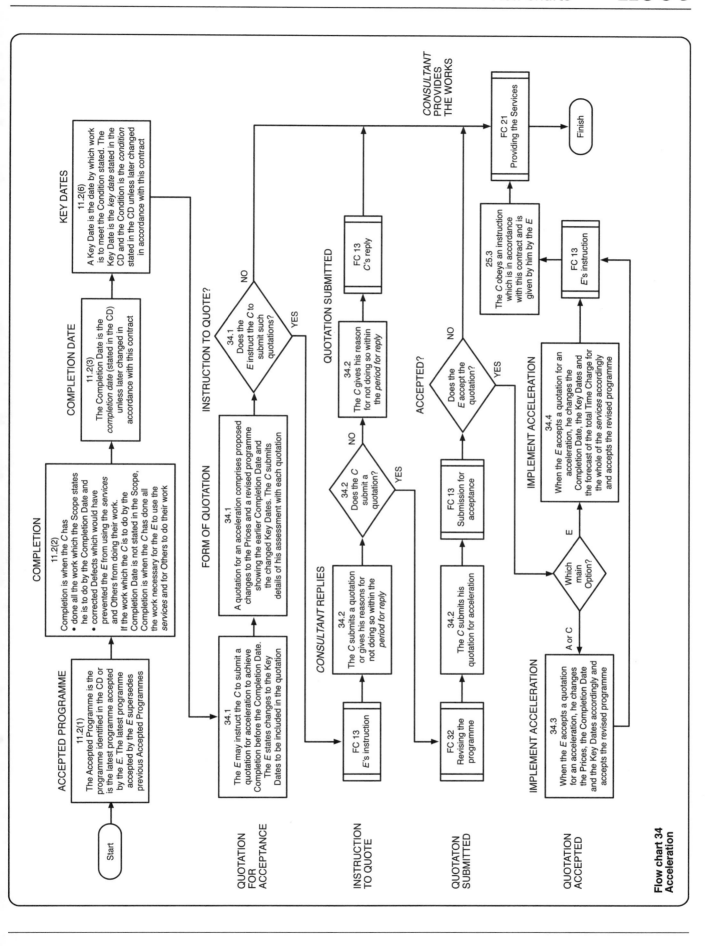

COMPLETION

11.2(2)

Completion is when the *C* has
• done all the work which the Scope states he is to do by the Completion Date and
• corrected Defects which would have prevented the *E* from using the *services* and Others from doing their work.
If the work which the *C* is to do by the Completion Date is not stated in the Scope, Completion is when the *C* has done all the work necessary for the *E* to use the *services* and for Others to do their work

COMPLETION DATE

11.2(3)

The Completion Date is the *completion date* (stated in the CD) unless later changed in accordance with this contract

KEY DATES

11.2(6)

A Key Date is the date by which work is to meet the Condition stated. The Key Date is the *key date* stated in the CD and the Condition is the *condition* stated in the CD unless later changed in accordance with this contract

ACCEPTED PROGRAMME

11.2(1)

The Accepted Programme is the programme identified in the CD or is the latest programme accepted by the *E*. The latest programme accepted by the *E* supersedes previous Accepted Programmes

Start

FORM OF QUOTATION

34.1

A quotation for an acceleration comprises proposed changes to the Prices and a revised programme showing the earlier Completion Date and the changed Key Dates. The *C* submits details of his assessment with each quotation

INSTRUCTION TO QUOTE?

34.1

Does the *E* instruct the *C* to submit such quotations?

NO / YES

QUOTATION FOR ACCEPTANCE

34.1

The *E* may instruct the *C* to submit a quotation for acceleration to achieve Completion before the Completion Date. The *E* states changes to the Key Dates to be included in the quotation

INSTRUCTION TO QUOTE

FC 13
E's instruction

CONSULTANT REPLIES

34.2

The *C* submits a quotation or gives his reasons for not doing so within the *period for reply*

34.2

Does the *C* submit a quotation?

NO / YES

QUOTATION SUBMITTED

34.2

The *C* gives his reason for not doing so within the *period for reply*

FC 13
C's reply

QUOTATON SUBMITTED

FC 32
Revising the programme

34.2

The *C* submits his quotation for acceleration

FC 13
Submission for acceptance

ACCEPTED?

34.2

Does the *E* accept the quotation?

NO / YES

QUOTATION ACCEPTED

IMPLEMENT ACCELERATION

34.3

When the *E* accepts a quotation for an acceleration, he changes the Prices, the Completion Date and the Key Dates accordingly and accepts the revised programme

A or C

Which main Option?

E

IMPLEMENT ACCELERATION

34.4

When the *E* accepts a quotation for an acceleration, he changes the Completion Date, the Key Dates and the forecast of the total Time Charge for the whole of the *services* accordingly and accepts the revised programme

FC 13
E's instruction

25.3

The *C* obeys an instruction which is in accordance with this contract and is given by him by the *E*

CONSULTANT PROVIDES THE WORKS

FC 21
Providing the Services

Finish

**Flow chart 34
Acceleration**

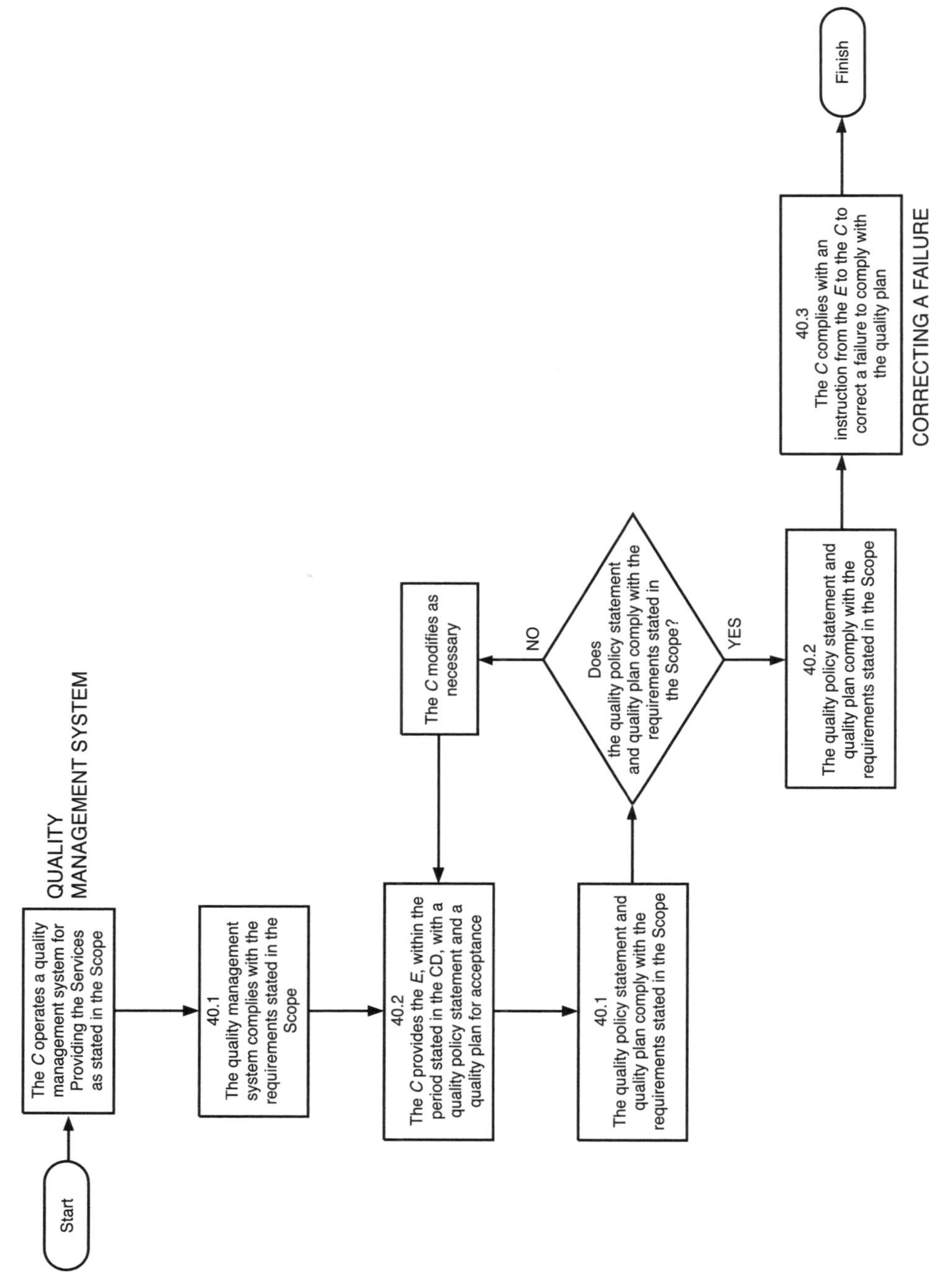

QUALITY
MANAGEMENT SYSTEM

```
┌─────────┐
│  Start  │
└─────────┘
     │
     ▼
┌──────────────────┐
│ The C operates a │
│ quality          │
│ management       │
│ system for       │
│ Providing the    │
│ Services         │
│ as stated in the │
│ Scope            │
└──────────────────┘
     │
     ▼
┌──────────────────┐
│ 40.1             │
│ The quality      │
│ management       │
│ system complies  │
│ with the         │
│ requirements     │
│ stated in the    │
│ Scope            │
└──────────────────┘
     │
     ▼
┌──────────────────┐
│ 40.2             │
│ The C provides   │
│ the E, within the│
│ period stated in │
│ the CD, with a   │
│ quality policy   │
│ statement and a  │
│ quality plan for │
│ acceptance       │
└──────────────────┘
     │
     ▼
┌──────────────────┐
│ 40.1             │
│ The quality      │
│ policy statement │
│ and quality plan │
│ comply with the  │
│ requirements     │
│ stated in the    │
│ Scope            │
└──────────────────┘
     │
     ▼
```

┌──────────────────┐
│ The C modifies as│
│ necessary   │
└──────────────────┘

Does the quality policy statement and quality plan comply with the requirements stated in the Scope?

NO

YES

┌──────────────────┐
│ 40.2   │
│ The quality   │
│ policy statement │
│ and quality plan │
│ comply with the │
│ requirements   │
│ stated in the   │
│ Scope   │
└──────────────────┘

┌──────────────────┐
│ 40.3   │
│ The C complies   │
│ with an   │
│ instruction from │
│ the E to the C to│
│ correct a failure│
│ to comply with   │
│ the quality plan │
└──────────────────┘
     │
     ▼
┌─────────┐
│ Finish │
└─────────┘

CORRECTING A FAILURE

Flow chart 40
Quality management system

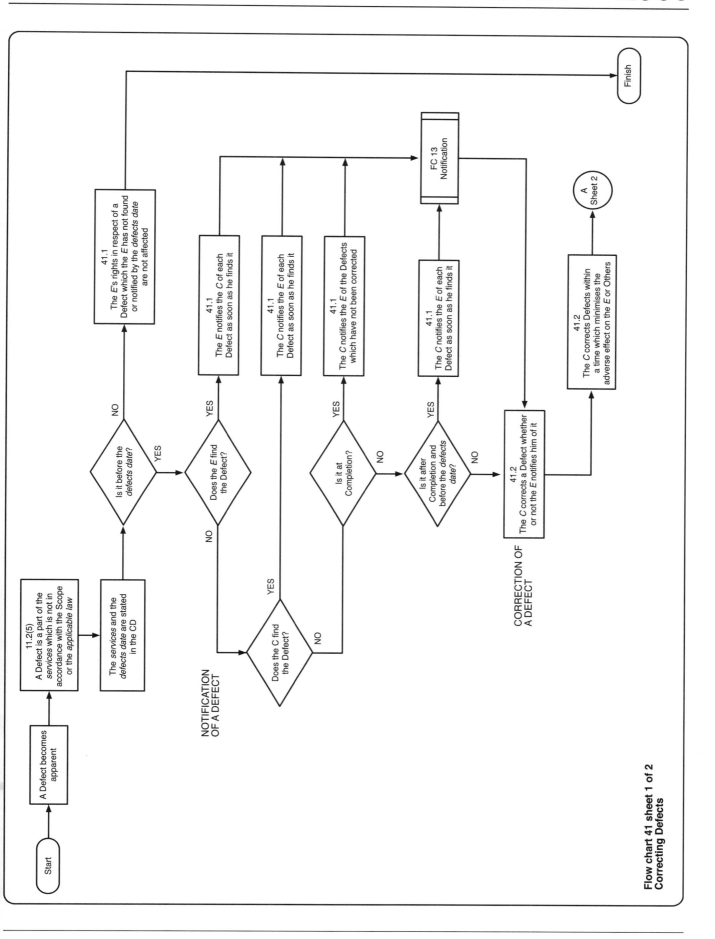

**Flow chart 41 sheet 1 of 2
Correcting Defects**

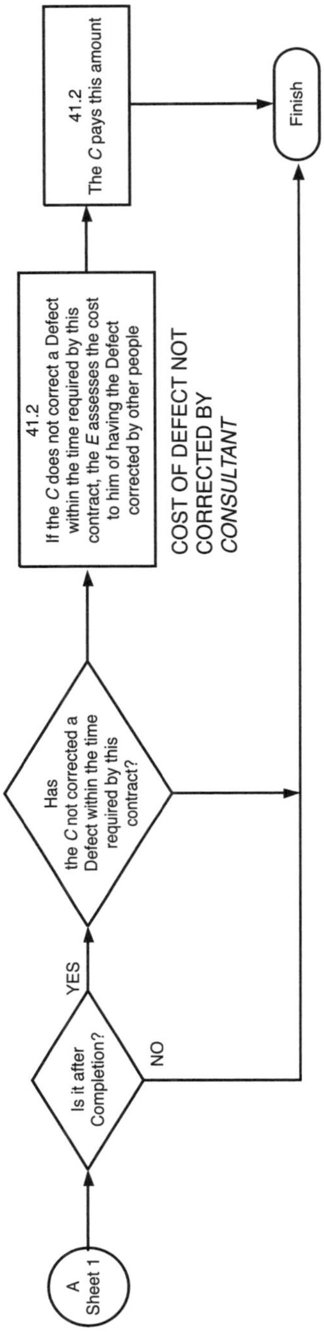

A
Sheet 1

Is it after
Completion?

YES

NO

Has
the C not corrected a
Defect within the time
required by this
contract?

41.2
If the C does not correct a Defect
within the time required by this
contract, the E assesses the cost
to him of having the Defect
corrected by other people

COST OF DEFECT NOT
CORRECTED BY
CONSULTANT

41.2
The C pays this amount

Finish

**Flow chart 41 Sheet 2 of 2
Correcting Defects**

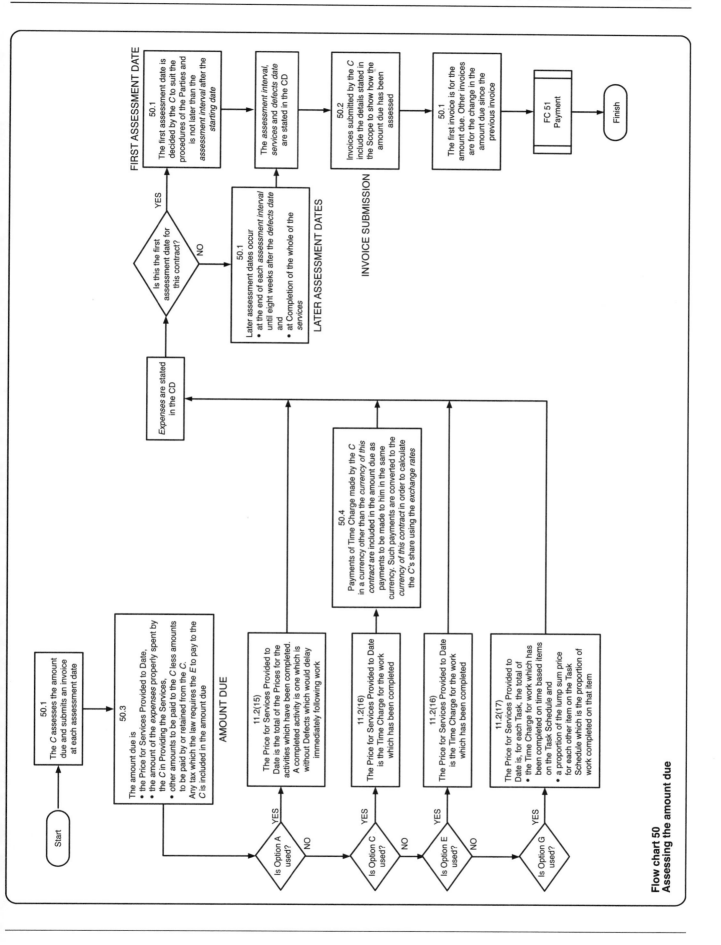

FIRST ASSESSMENT DATE

50.1
The first assessment date is decided by the *C* to suit the procedures of the Parties and is not later than the *assessment interval* after the *starting date*

The *assessment interval*, *services* and *defects date* are stated in the CD

LATER ASSESSMENT DATES

50.1
Is this the first assessment date for this contract?

YES

NO

50.1
Later assessment dates occur
• at the end of each *assessment interval* until eight weeks after the *defects date* and
• at Completion of the whole of the *services*

INVOICE SUBMISSION

50.2
Invoices submitted by the *C* include the details stated in the Scope to show how the amount due has been assessed

50.1
The first invoice is for the amount due. Other invoices are for the change in the amount due since the previous invoice

FC 51
Payment

Finish

Expenses are stated in the CD

50.4
Payments of Time Charge made by the *C* in a currency other than the *currency of this contract* are included in the amount due as payments to be made to him in the same currency. Such payments are converted to the *currency of this contract* in order to calculate the *C*'s share using the *exchange rates*

Start

50.1
The *C* assesses the amount due and submits an invoice at each assessment date

50.3
The amount due is
• the Price for Services Provided to Date,
• the amount of the *expenses* properly spent by the *C* in Providing the Services,
• other amounts to be paid to the *C* less amounts to be paid by or retained from the *C*.
Any tax which the law requires the *E* to pay to the *C* is included in the amount due

AMOUNT DUE

11.2(15)
The Price for Services Provided to Date is the total of the Prices for the activities which have been completed. A completed activity is one which is without Defects which would delay immediately following work

Is Option A used?

YES

NO

11.2(16)
The Price for Services Provided to Date is the Time Charge for the work which has been completed

Is Option C used?

YES

NO

11.2(16)
The Price for Services Provided to Date is the Time Charge for the work which has been completed

Is Option E used?

YES

NO

11.2(17)
The Price for Services Provided to Date is, for each Task, the total of
• the Time Charge for work which has been completed on time based items on the Task Schedule and
• a proportion of the lump sum price for each other item on the Task Schedule which is the proportion of work completed on that item

Is Option G used?

YES

Flow chart 50
Assessing the amount due

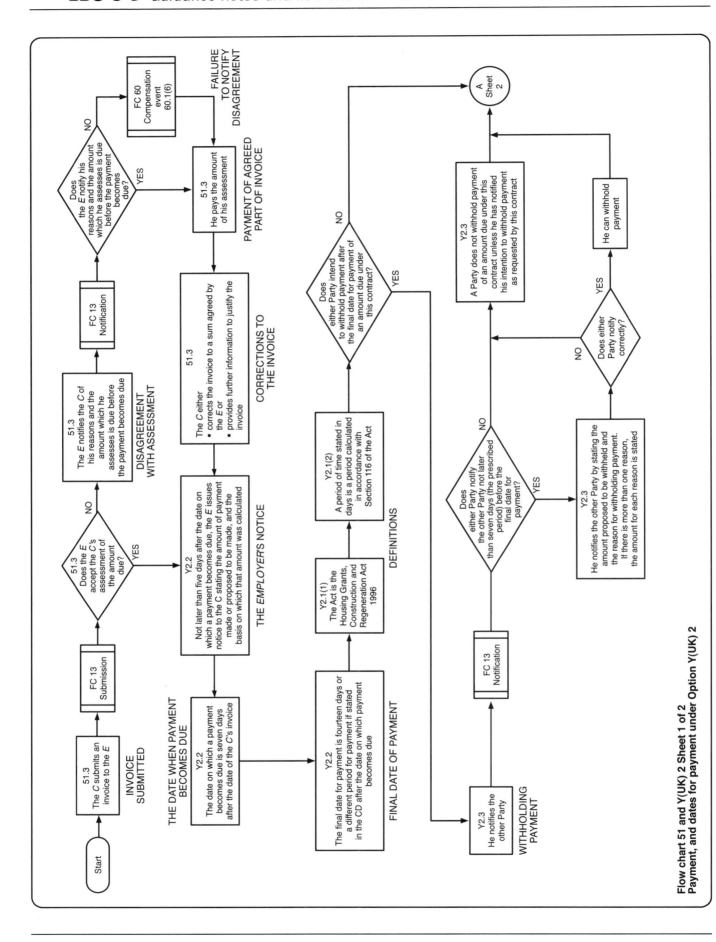

Start

51.3
The *C* submits an invoice to the *E*

INVOICE SUBMITTED

FC 13
Submission

51.3
Does the *E* accept the *C's* assessment of the amount due?

NO →

51.3
The *E* notifies the *C* of his reasons and the amount which he assesses is due before the payment becomes due

DISAGREEMENT WITH ASSESSMENT

FC 13
Notification

Does the *E* notify his reasons and the amount which he assesses is due before the payment becomes due?

NO →

FC 60
Compensation event 60.1(6)

FAILURE TO NOTIFY DISAGREEMENT

YES ↓

51.3
He pays the amount of his assessment

PAYMENT OF AGREED PART OF INVOICE

YES (from amount due) →

51.3
The *C* either
• corrects the invoice to a sum agreed by the *E* or
• provides further information to justify the invoice

CORRECTIONS TO THE INVOICE

Y2.2
Not later than five days after the date on which a payment becomes due, the *E* issues a notice to the *C* stating the amount of payment made or proposed to be made, and the basis on which that amount was calculated

THE *EMPLOYER'S* NOTICE

Y2.2
The date on which a payment becomes due is seven days after the date of the *C's* invoice

THE DATE WHEN PAYMENT BECOMES DUE

Y2.2
The final date for payment is fourteen days or a different period for payment if stated in the CD after the date on which payment becomes due

FINAL DATE OF PAYMENT

Y2.1(1)
The Act is the Housing Grants, Construction and Regeneration Act 1996

Y2.1(2)
A period of time stated in days is a period calculated in accordance with Section 116 of the Act

DEFINITIONS

Does either Party intend to withhold payment after the final date for payment of an amount due under this contract?

NO → A Sheet 2

YES ↓

Y2.3
He notifies the other Party

WITHHOLDING PAYMENT

FC 13
Notification

Does either Party notify the other Party not later than seven days (the prescribed period) before the final date for payment?

NO →

Y2.3
A Party does not withhold payment of an amount due under this contract unless he has notified his intention to withhold payment as requested by this contract

→ A Sheet 2

YES ↓

Y2.3
He notifies the other Party by stating the amount proposed to be withheld and the reason for withholding payment. If there is more than one reason, the amount for each reason is stated

Does either Party notify correctly?

NO → A Sheet 2

YES ↓

He can withhold payment

→ A Sheet 2

Flow chart 51 and Y(UK) 2 Sheet 1 of 2
Payment, and dates for payment under Option Y(UK) 2

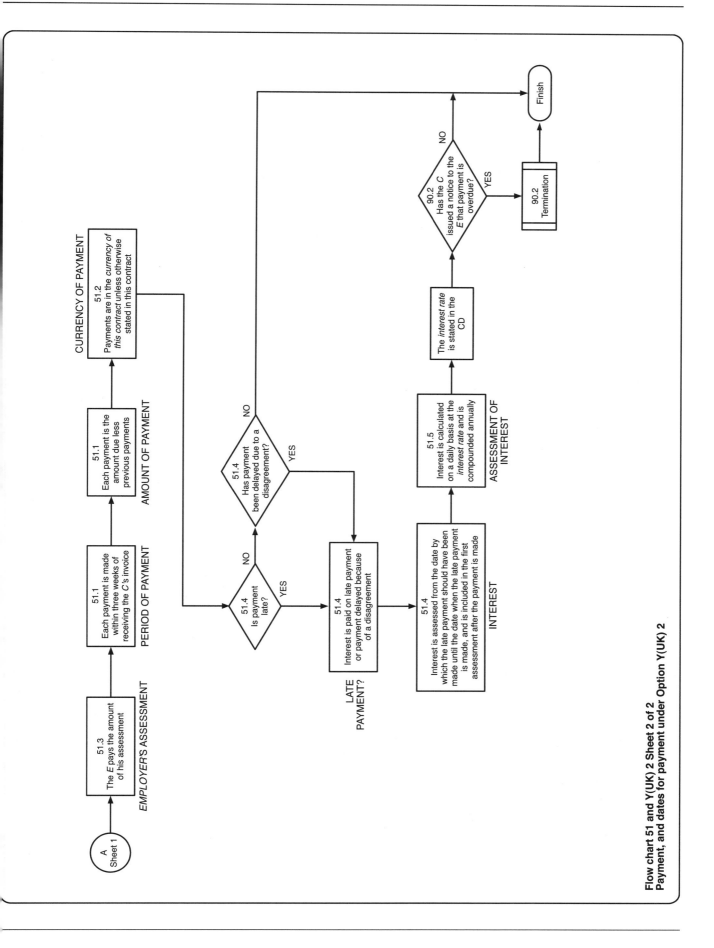

Flow chart 51 and Y(UK) 2 Sheet 2 of 2
Payment, and dates for payment under Option Y(UK) 2

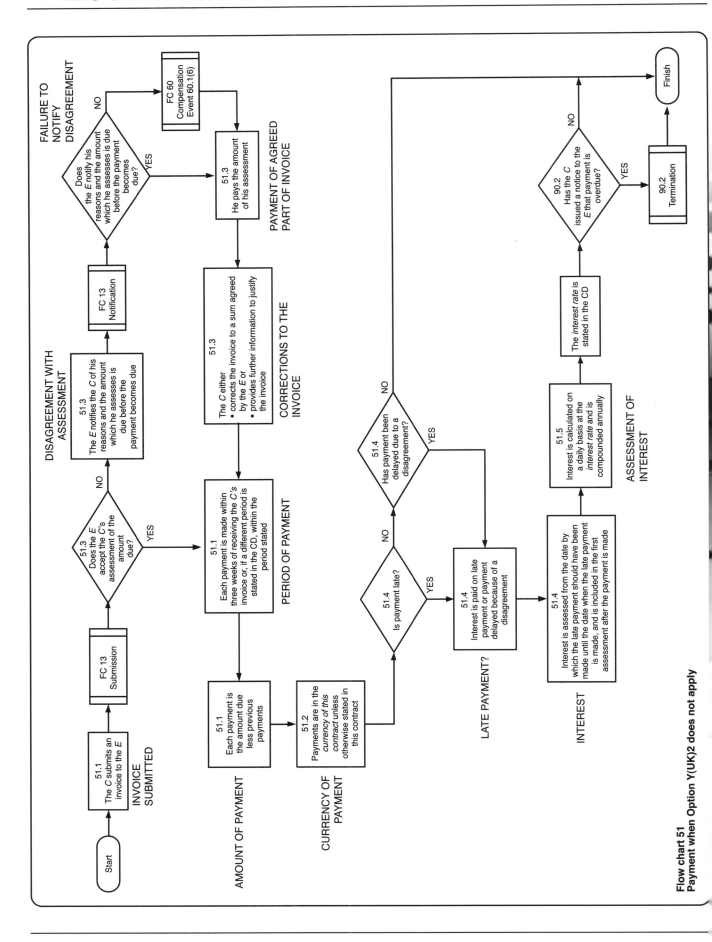

Flow chart 51
Payment when Option Y(UK)2 does not apply

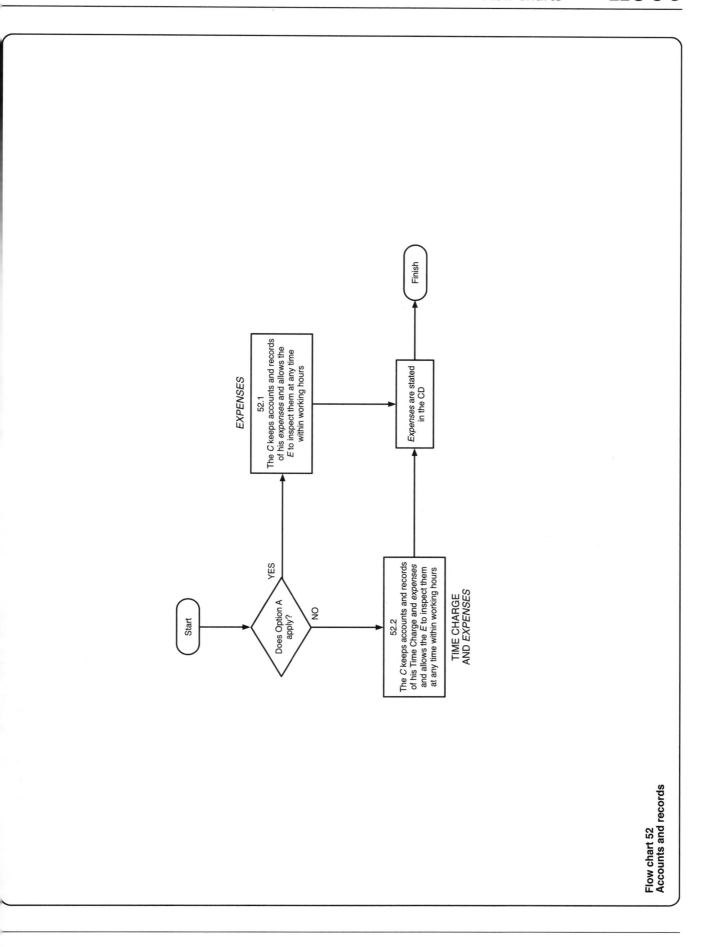

Start

Does Option A apply?

YES

NO

EXPENSES

52.1
The *C* keeps accounts and records of his *expenses* and allows the *E* to inspect them at any time within working hours

52.2
The *C* keeps accounts and records of his Time Charge and *expenses* and allows the *E* to inspect them at any time within working hours

TIME CHARGE
AND *EXPENSES*

Expenses are stated in the CD

Finish

**Flow chart 52
Accounts and records**

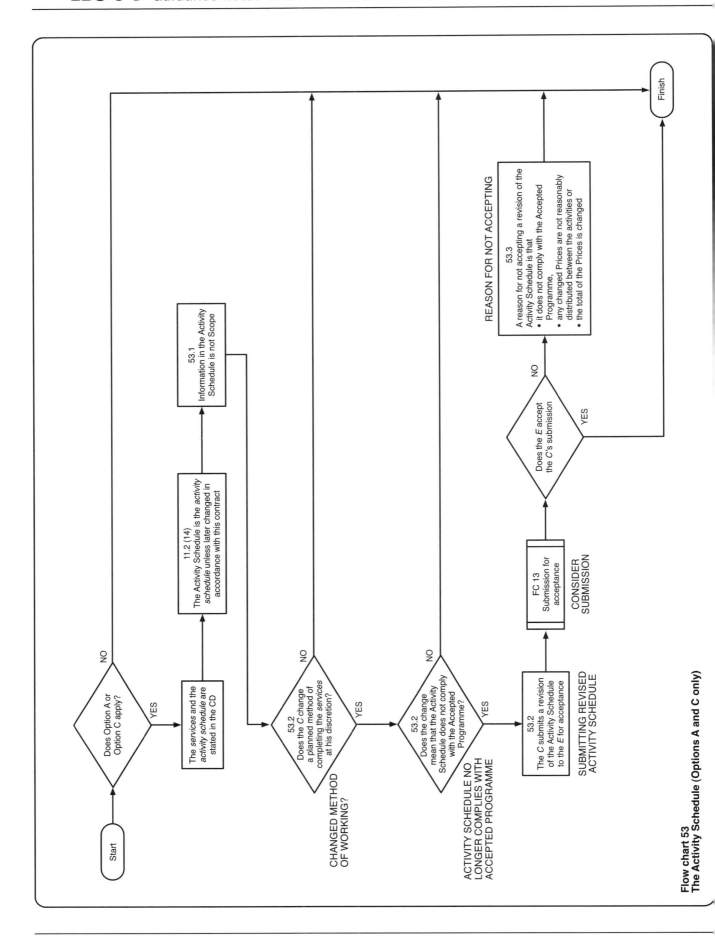

Flow chart 53
The Activity Schedule (Options A and C only)

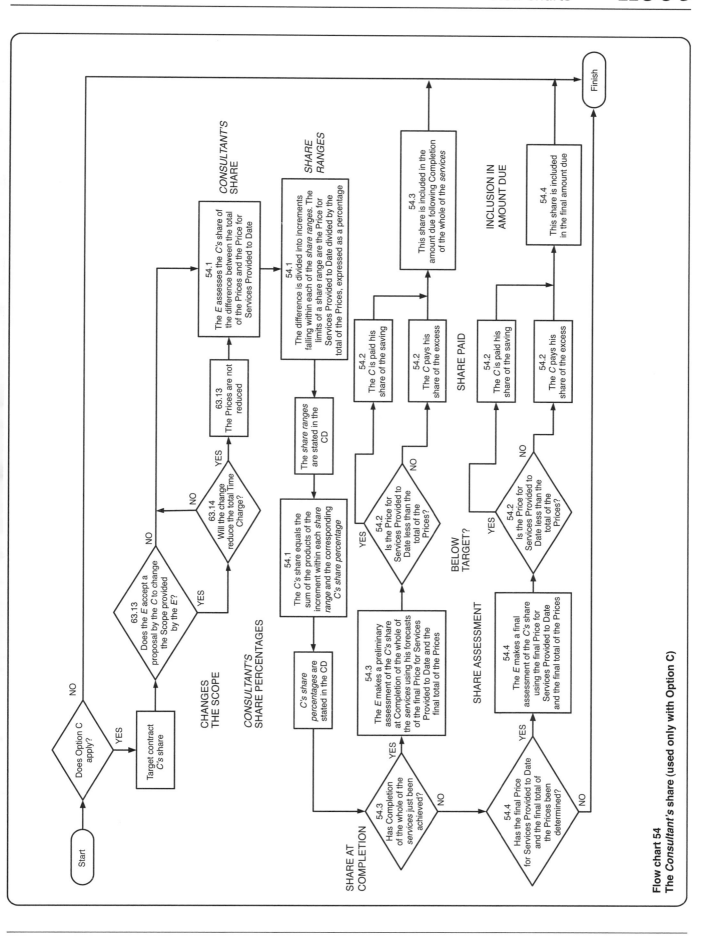

Flow chart 54
The *Consultant's* share (used only with Option C)

 91

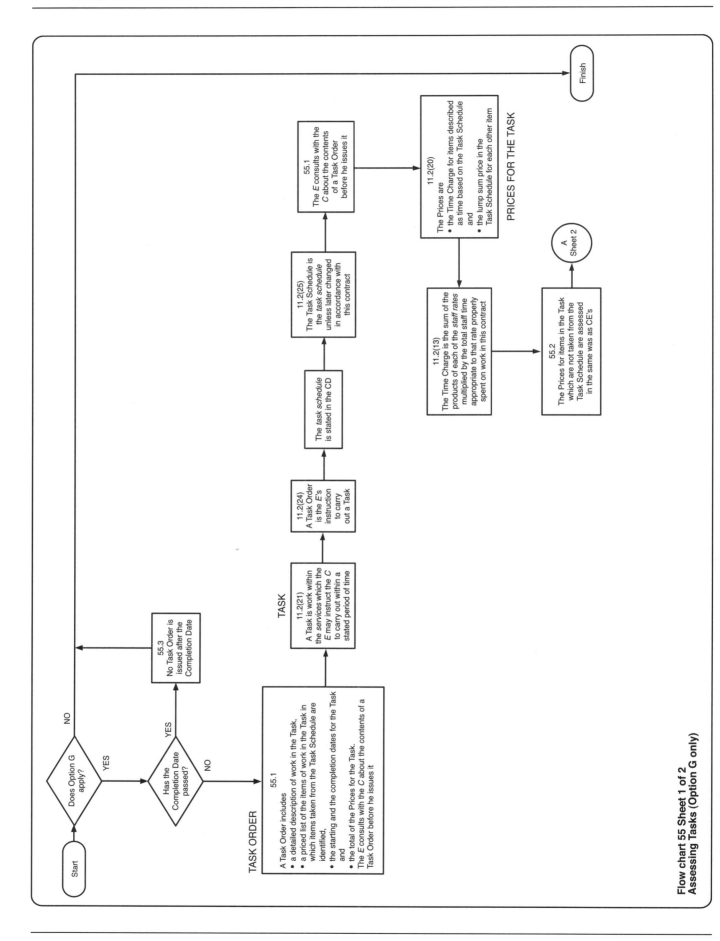

TASK ORDER

55.1

A Task Order includes
- a detailed description of work in the Task,
- a priced list of the items of work in the Task in which items taken from the Task Schedule are identified,
- the starting and the completion dates for the Task and
- the total of the Prices for the Task.

The E consults with the C about the contents of a Task Order before he issues it

TASK

11.2(21)

A Task is work within the *services* which the E may instruct the C to carry out within a stated period of time

11.2(24)

A Task Order is the E's instruction to carry out a Task

The *task schedule* is stated in the CD

11.2(25)

The Task Schedule is the *task schedule* unless later changed in accordance with this contract

55.1

The E consults with the C about the contents of a Task Order before he issues it

PRICES FOR THE TASK

11.2(20)

The Prices are
- the Time Charge for items described as time based on the Task Schedule and
- the lump sum price in the Task Schedule for each other item

11.2(13)

The Time Charge is the sum of the products of each of the *staff rates* multiplied by the total staff time appropriate to that rate properly spent on work in this contract

55.2

The Prices for items in the Task which are not taken from the Task Schedule are assessed in the same was as CE's

A Sheet 2

Start

Does Option G apply? — NO / YES

Has the Completion Date passed? — YES / NO

55.3

No Task Order is issued after the Completion Date

Finish

Flow chart 55 Sheet 1 of 2
Assessing Tasks (Option G only)

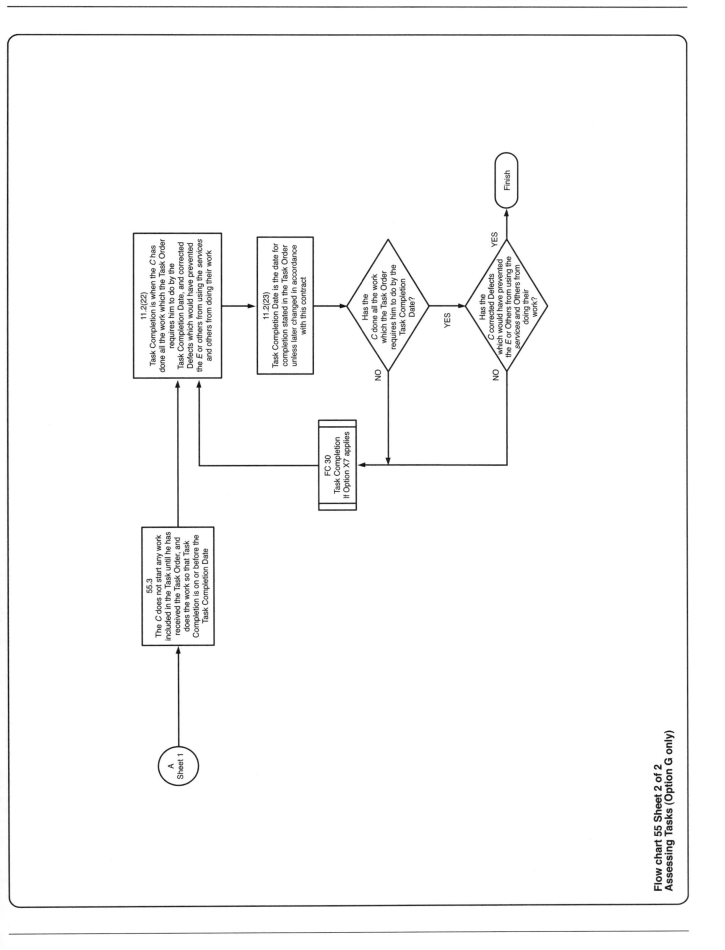

Flow chart 55 Sheet 2 of 2
Assessing Tasks (Option G only)

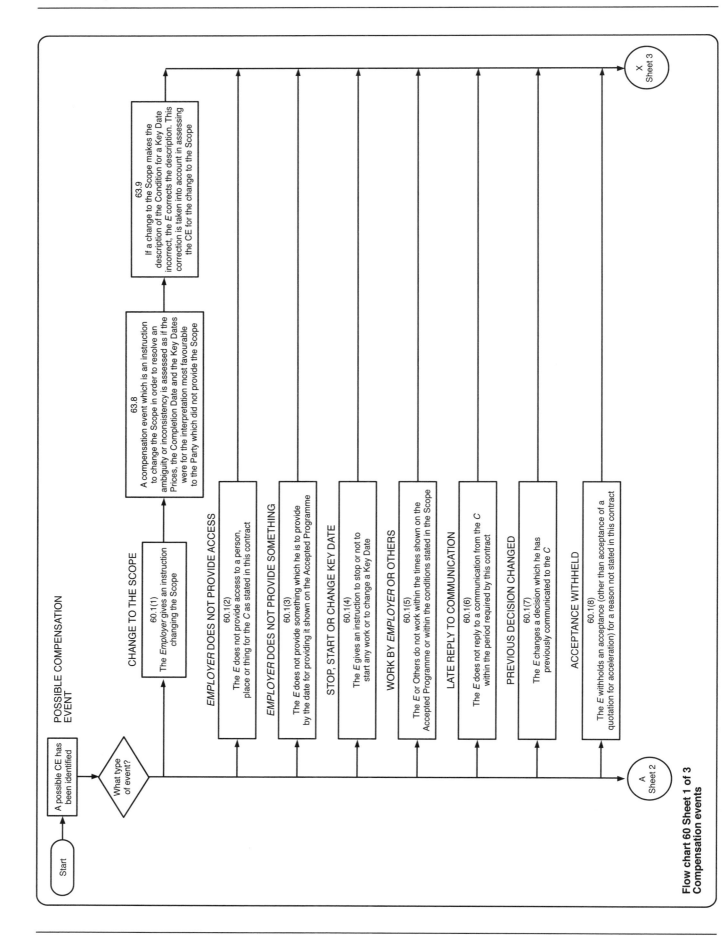

63.9
If a change to the Scope makes the description of the Condition for a Key Date incorrect, the *E* corrects the description. This correction is taken into account in assessing the CE for the change to the Scope

63.8
A compensation event which is an instruction to change the Scope in order to resolve an ambiguity or inconsistency is assessed as if the Prices, the Completion Date and the Key Dates were for the interpretation most favourable to the Party which did not provide the Scope

POSSIBLE COMPENSATION EVENT

A possible CE has been identified

Start

What type of event?

CHANGE TO THE SCOPE

60.1(1)
The *Employer* gives an instruction changing the Scope

EMPLOYER DOES NOT PROVIDE ACCESS

60.1(2)
The *E* does not provide access to a person, place or thing for the *C* as stated in this contract

EMPLOYER DOES NOT PROVIDE SOMETHING

60.1(3)
The *E* does not provide something which he is to provide by the date for providing it shown on the Accepted Programme

STOP, START OR CHANGE KEY DATE

60.1(4)
The *E* gives an instruction to stop or not to start any work or to change a Key Date

WORK BY *EMPLOYER* OR OTHERS

60.1(5)
The *E* or Others do not work within the times shown on the Accepted Programme or within the conditions stated in the Scope

LATE REPLY TO COMMUNICATION

60.1(6)
The *E* does not reply to a communication from the *C* within the period required by this contract

PREVIOUS DECISION CHANGED

60.1(7)
The *E* changes a decision which he has previously communicated to the *C*

ACCEPTANCE WITHHELD

60.1(8)
The *E* withholds an acceptance (other than acceptance of a quotation for acceleration) for a reason not stated in this contract

X
Sheet 3

A
Sheet 2

Flow chart 60 Sheet 1 of 3
Compensation events

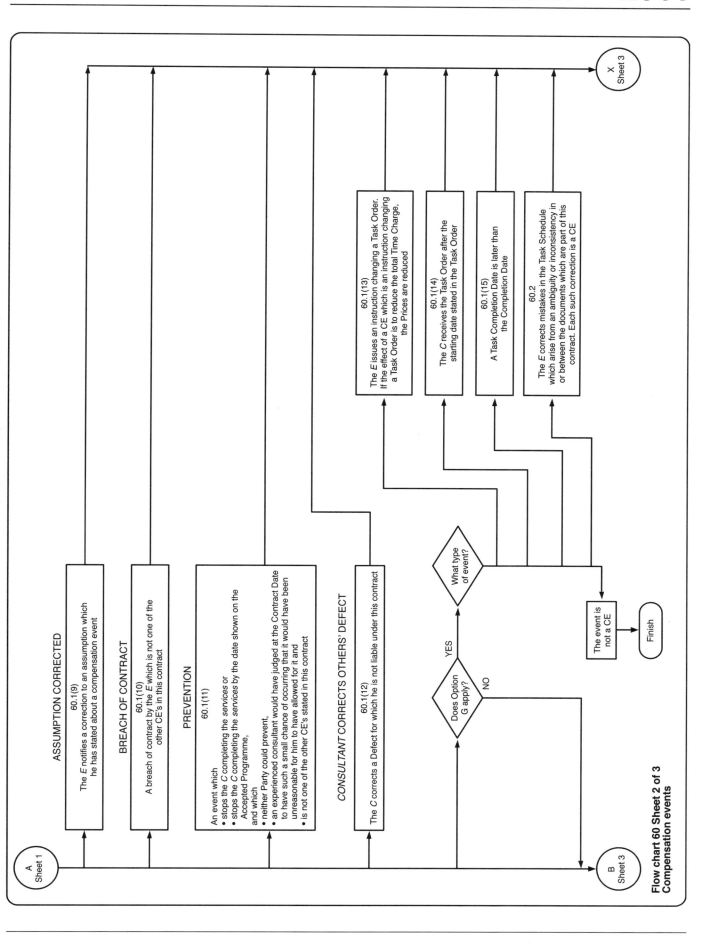

ASSUMPTION CORRECTED

60.1(9)

The *E* notifies a correction to an assumption which he has stated about a compensation event

BREACH OF CONTRACT

60.1(10)

A breach of contract by the *E* which is not one of the other CE's in this contract

PREVENTION

60.1(11)

An event which
• stops the *C* completing the *services* or
• stops the *C* completing the *services* by the date shown on the Accepted Programme,
and which
• neither Party could prevent,
• an experienced consultant would have judged at the Contract Date to have such a small chance of occurring that it would have been unreasonable for him to have allowed for it and
• is not one of the other CE's stated in this contract

CONSULTANT CORRECTS OTHERS' DEFECT

60.1(12)

The *C* corrects a Defect for which he is not liable under this contract

60.1(13)

The *E* issues an instruction changing a Task Order. If the effect of a CE which is an instruction changing a Task Order is to reduce the total Time Charge, the Prices are reduced

60.1(14)

The *C* receives the Task Order after the starting date stated in the Task Order

60.1(15)

A Task Completion Date is later than the Completion Date

60.2

The *E* corrects mistakes in the Task Schedule which arise from an ambiguity or inconsistency in or between the documents which are part of this contract. Each such correction is a CE

Does Option G apply?

YES

NO

What type of event?

The event is not a CE

Finish

A Sheet 1

B Sheet 3

X Sheet 3

Flow chart 60 Sheet 2 of 3
Compensation events

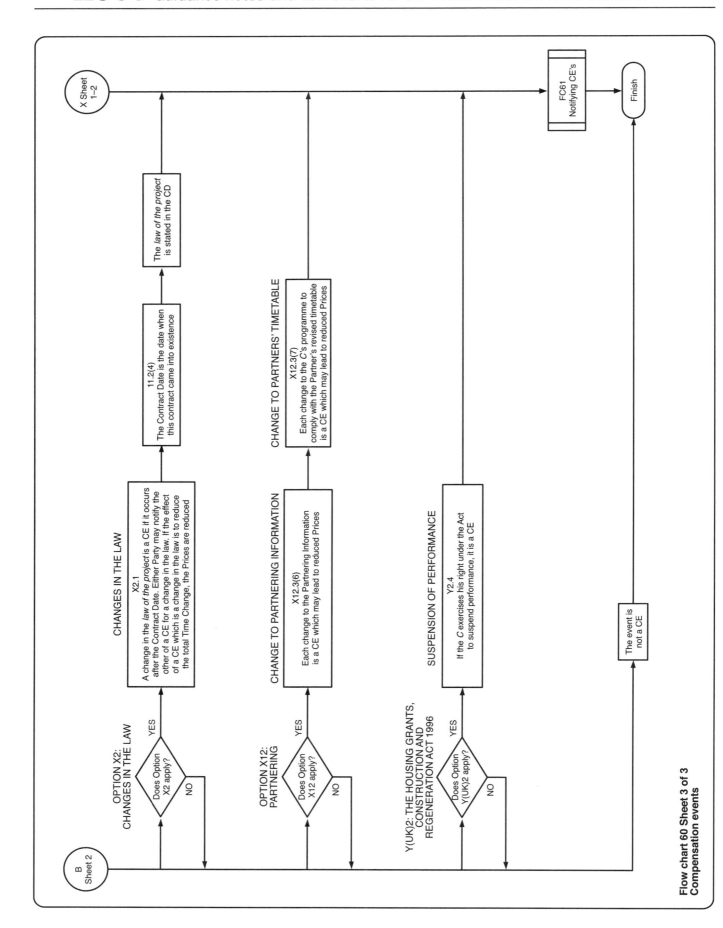

Flow chart 60 Sheet 3 of 3
Compensation events

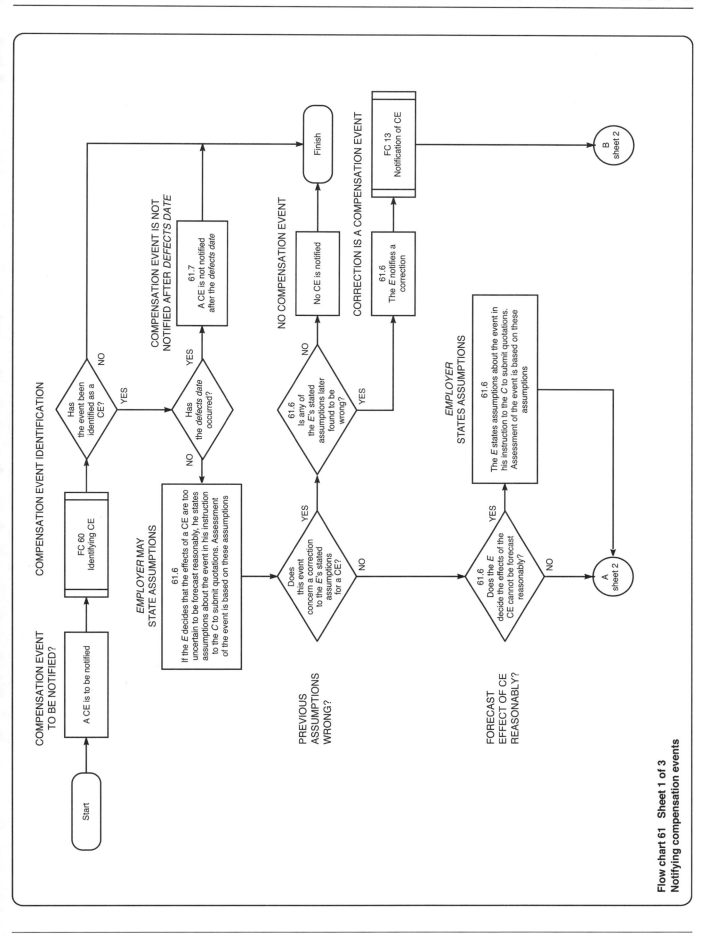

COMPENSATION EVENT TO BE NOTIFIED?

Start

A CE is to be notified

COMPENSATION EVENT IDENTIFICATION

FC 60
Identifying CE

Has the event been identified as a CE? — NO

YES

COMPENSATION EVENT IS NOT NOTIFIED AFTER *DEFECTS DATE*

Has the *defects date* occurred?

YES

61.7
A CE is not notified after the *defects date*

NO

Finish

EMPLOYER MAY STATE ASSUMPTIONS

61.6
If the *E* decides that the effects of a CE are too uncertain to be forecast reasonably, he states assumptions about the event in his instruction to the *C* to submit quotations. Assessment of the event is based on these assumptions

PREVIOUS ASSUMPTIONS WRONG?

Does this event concern a correction to the *E*'s stated assumptions for a CE?

YES

61.6
Is any of the *E*'s stated assumptions later found to be wrong?

NO

NO COMPENSATION EVENT

No CE is notified

YES

CORRECTION IS A COMPENSATION EVENT

61.6
The *E* notifies a correction

FC 13
Notification of CE

B
sheet 2

NO

FORECAST EFFECT OF CE REASONABLY?

61.6
Does the *E* decide the effects of the CE cannot be forecast reasonably?

YES

EMPLOYER STATES ASSUMPTIONS

61.6
The *E* states assumptions about the event in his instruction to the *C* to submit quotations. Assessment of the event is based on these assumptions

NO

A
sheet 2

Flow chart 61   Sheet 1 of 3
Notifying compensation events

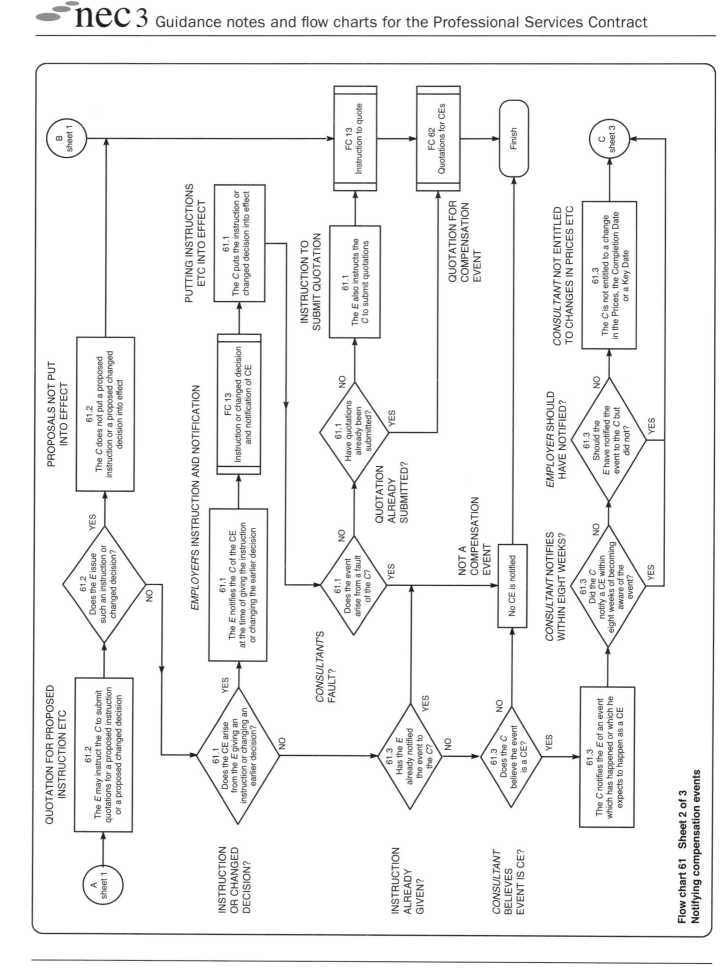

QUOTATION FOR PROPOSED INSTRUCTION ETC

PROPOSALS NOT PUT INTO EFFECT

PUTTING INSTRUCTIONS ETC INTO EFFECT

EMPLOYER'S INSTRUCTION AND NOTIFICATION

INSTRUCTION TO SUBMIT QUOTATION

QUOTATION FOR COMPENSATION EVENT

CONSULTANT'S FAULT?

NOT A COMPENSATION EVENT

CONSULTANT NOTIFIES WITHIN EIGHT WEEKS?

EMPLOYER SHOULD HAVE NOTIFIED?

CONSULTANT NOT ENTITLED TO CHANGES IN PRICES ETC

INSTRUCTION OR CHANGED DECISION?

INSTRUCTION ALREADY GIVEN?

CONSULTANT BELIEVES EVENT IS CE?

A
sheet 1

61.2
The *E* may instruct the *C* to submit quotations for a proposed instruction or a proposed changed decision

61.2
Does the *E* issue such an instruction or changed decision?

61.2
The *C* does not put a proposed instruction or a proposed changed decision into effect

61.1
The *C* puts the instruction or changed decision into effect

61.1
The *E* notifies the *C* of the CE at the time of giving the instruction or changing the earlier decision

FC 13
Instruction or changed decision and notification of CE

FC 13
Instruction to quote

FC 62
Quotations for CEs

Finish

61.1
Does the CE arise from the *E* giving an instruction or changing an earlier decision?

61.1
Does the event arise from a fault of the *C*?

61.1
Have quotations already been submitted?

The *E* also instructs the *C* to submit quotations

61.3
Has the *E* already notified the event to the *C*?

No CE is notified

61.3
Does the *C* believe the event is a CE?

61.3
The *C* notifies the *E* of an event which has happened or which he expects to happen as a CE

61.3
Did the *C* notify a CE within eight weeks of becoming aware of the event?

61.3
Should the *E* have notified the event to the *C* but did not?

61.3
The *C* is not entitled to a change in the Prices, the Completion Date or a Key Date

B
sheet 1

C
sheet 3

**Flow chart 61   Sheet 2 of 3
Notifying compensation events**

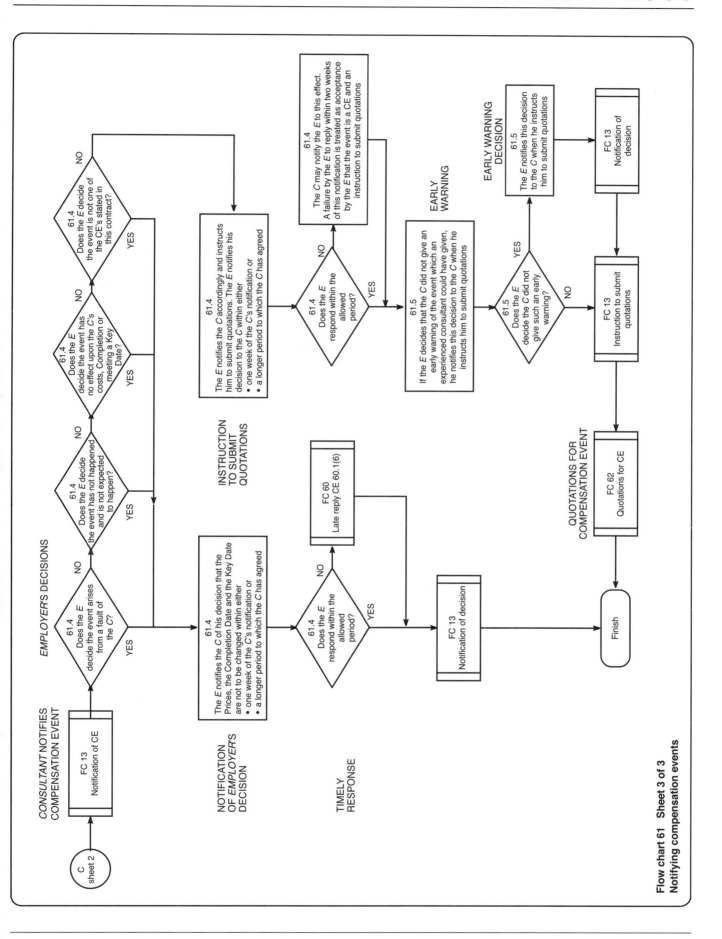

Flow chart 61   Sheet 3 of 3
Notifying compensation events

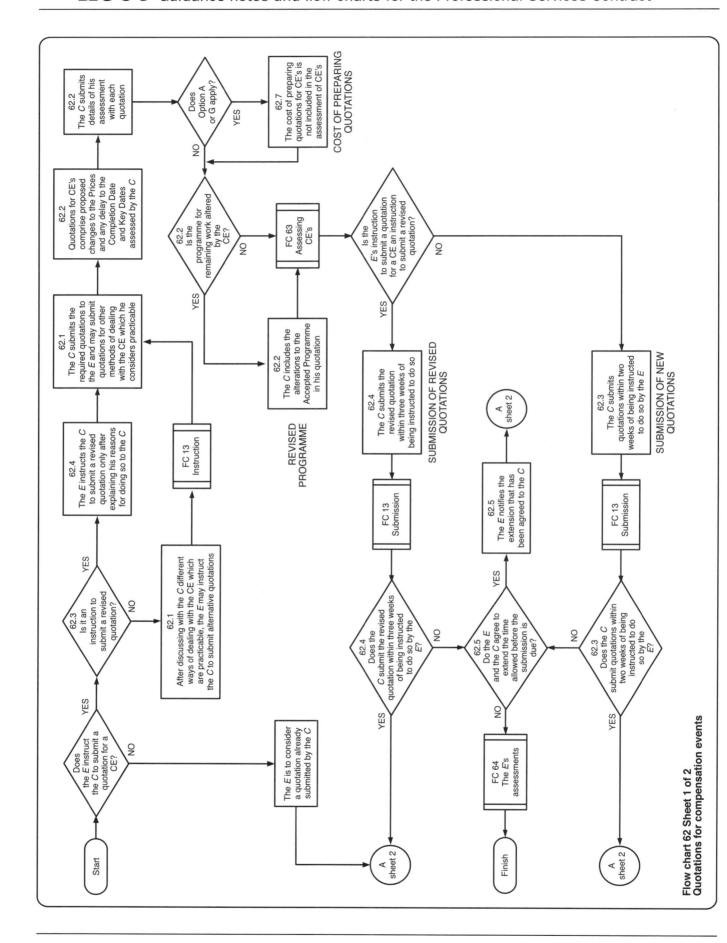

COST OF PREPARING QUOTATIONS

62.7
The cost of preparing quotations for CE's is not included in the assessment of CE's

62.2
Does Option A or G apply?

62.2
The C submits details of his assessment with each quotation

62.2
Quotations for CE's comprise proposed changes to the Prices and any delay to the Completion Date and Key Dates assessed by the C

62.1
The C submits the required quotations to the E and may submit quotations for other methods of dealing with the CE which he considers practicable

62.4
The E instructs the C to submit a revised quotation only after explaining his reasons for doing so to the C

62.3
Is it an instruction to submit a revised quotation?

62.1
After discussing with the C different ways of dealing with the CE which are practicable, the E may instruct the C to submit alternative quotations

FC 13
Instruction

62.2
Is the programme for remaining work altered by the CE?

62.2
The C includes the alterations to the Accepted Programme in his quotation

REVISED PROGRAMME

FC 63
Assessing CE's

Is the E's instruction to submit a quotation for a CE an instruction to submit a revised quotation?

62.4
The C submits the revised quotation within three weeks of being instructed to do so

SUBMISSION OF REVISED QUOTATIONS

FC 13
Submission

62.4
Does the C submit the revised quotation within three weeks of being instructed to do so by the E?

62.5
Do the E and the C agree to extend the time allowed before the submission is due?

62.5
The E notifies the extension that has been agreed to the C

A
sheet 2

62.3
The C submits quotations within two weeks of being instructed to do so by the E

SUBMISSION OF NEW QUOTATIONS

FC 13
Submission

62.3
Does the C submit quotations within two weeks of being instructed to do so by the E?

FC 64
The E's assessments

Does the E instruct the C to submit a quotation for a CE?

The E is to consider a quotation already submitted by the C

Start

A
sheet 2

Finish

A
sheet 2

Flow chart 62 Sheet 1 of 2
Quotations for compensation events

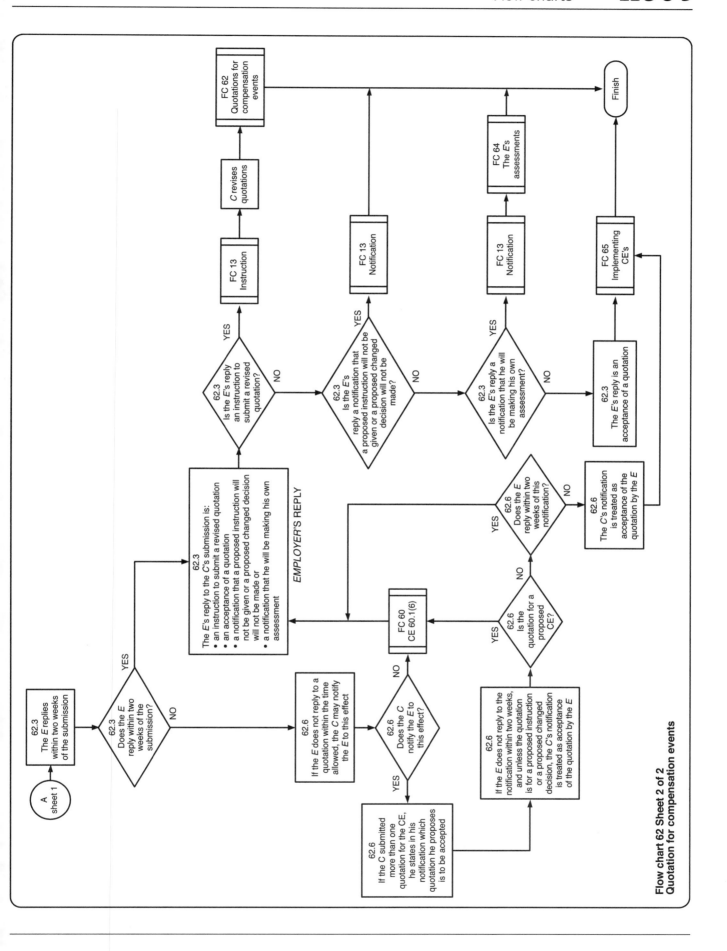

Flow chart 62 Sheet 2 of 2
Quotation for compensation events

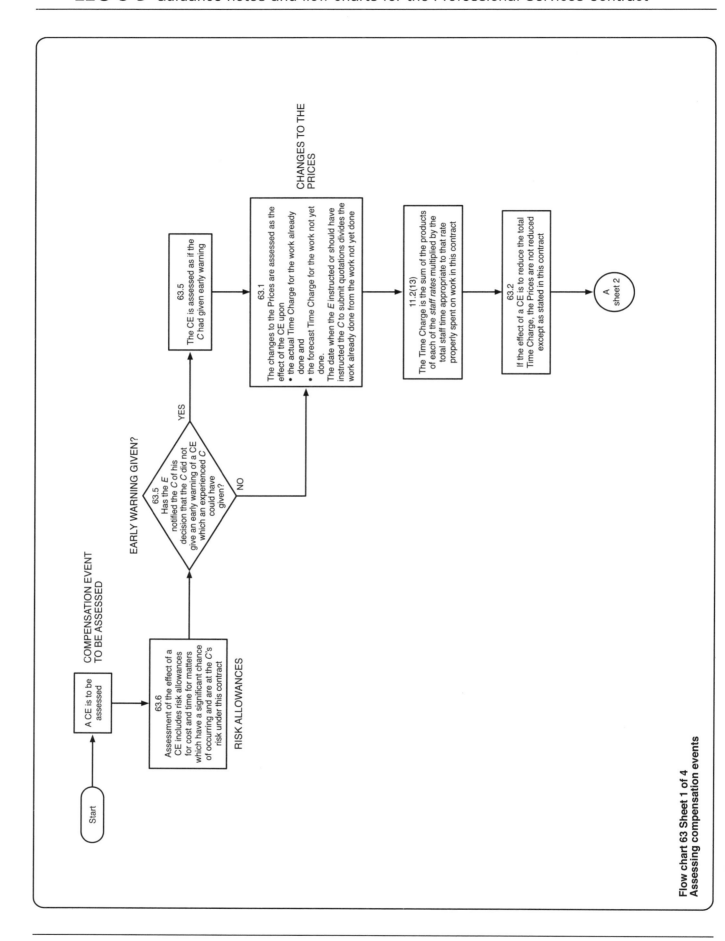

COMPENSATION EVENT TO BE ASSESSED

Start

A CE is to be assessed

63.6
Assessment of the effect of a CE includes risk allowances for cost and time for matters which have a significant chance of occurring and are at the C's risk under this contract

RISK ALLOWANCES

EARLY WARNING GIVEN?

63.5
Has the E notified the C of his decision that the C did not give an early warning of a CE which an experienced C could have given?

YES

NO

63.5
The CE is assessed as if the C had given early warning

63.1
The changes to the Prices are assessed as the effect of the CE upon
• the actual Time Charge for the work already done and
• the forecast Time Charge for the work not yet done.
The date when the E instructed or should have instructed the C to submit quotations divides the work already done from the work not yet done

CHANGES TO THE PRICES

11.2(13)
The Time Charge is the sum of the products of each of the *staff rates* multiplied by the total staff time appropriate to that rate properly spent on work in this contract

63.2
If the effect of a CE is to reduce the total Time Charge, the Prices are not reduced except as stated in this contract

A
sheet 2

Flow chart 63 Sheet 1 of 4
Assessing compensation events

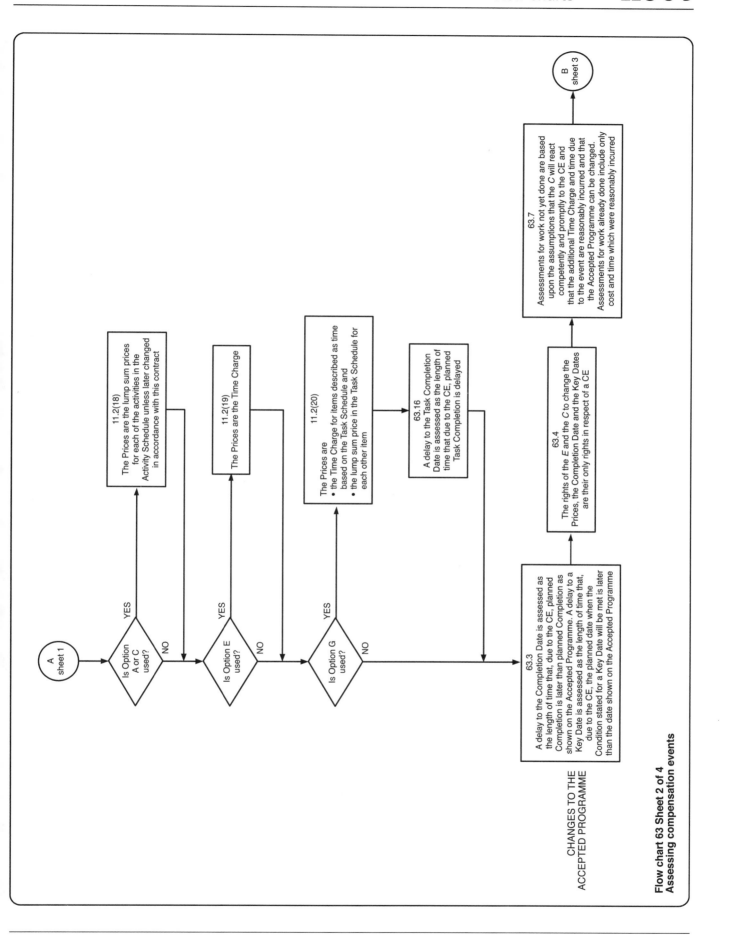

11.2(18)

The Prices are the lump sum prices for each of the activities in the Activity Schedule unless later changed in accordance with this contract

11.2(19)

The Prices are the Time Charge

11.2(20)

The Prices are
- the Time Charge for items described as time based on the Task Schedule and
- the lump sum price in the Task Schedule for each other item

63.16

A delay to the Task Completion Date is assessed as the length of time that due to the CE, planned Task Completion is delayed

63.7

Assessments for work not yet done are based upon the assumptions that the *C* will react competently and promptly to the CE and that the additional Time Charge and time due to the event are reasonably incurred and that the Accepted Programme can be changed. Assessments for work already done include only cost and time which were reasonably incurred

63.4

The rights of the *E* and the *C* to change the Prices, the Completion Date and the Key Dates are their only rights in respect of a CE

63.3

A delay to the Completion Date is assessed as the length of time that, due to the CE, planned Completion is later than planned Completion as shown on the Accepted Programme. A delay to a Key Date is assessed as the length of time that, due to the CE, the planned date when the Condition stated for a Key Date will be met is later than the date shown on the Accepted Programme

A
sheet 1

YES

Is Option A or C used?

NO

YES

Is Option E used?

NO

YES

Is Option G used?

NO

B
sheet 3

CHANGES TO THE ACCEPTED PROGRAMME

Flow chart 63 Sheet 2 of 4
Assessing compensation events

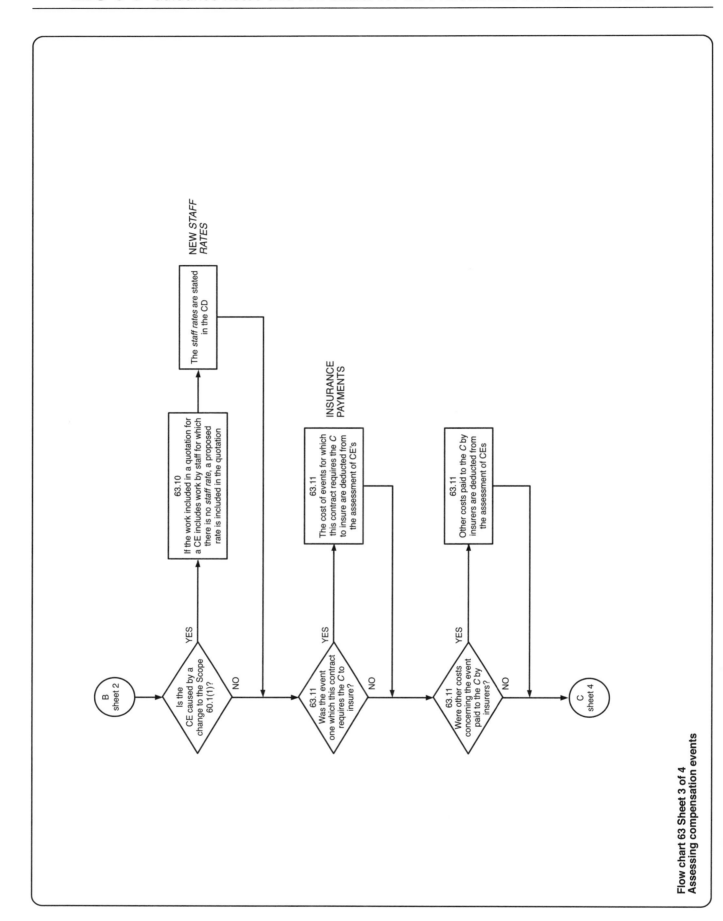

NEW STAFF
RATES

The *staff rates* are stated
in the CD

63.10
If the work included in a quotation for
a CE includes work by staff for which
there is no *staff rate*, a proposed
rate is included in the quotation

YES

B
sheet 2

Is the
CE caused by a
change to the Scope
60.1(1)?

NO

INSURANCE
PAYMENTS

63.11
The cost of events for which
this contract requires the C
to insure are deducted from
the assessment of CE's

YES

63.11
Was the event
one which this contract
requires the C to
insure?

NO

63.11
Other costs paid to the C by
insurers are deducted from
the assessment of CEs

YES

63.11
Were other costs
concerning the event
paid to the C by
insurers?

NO

C
sheet 4

Flow chart 63 Sheet 3 of 4
Assessing compensation events

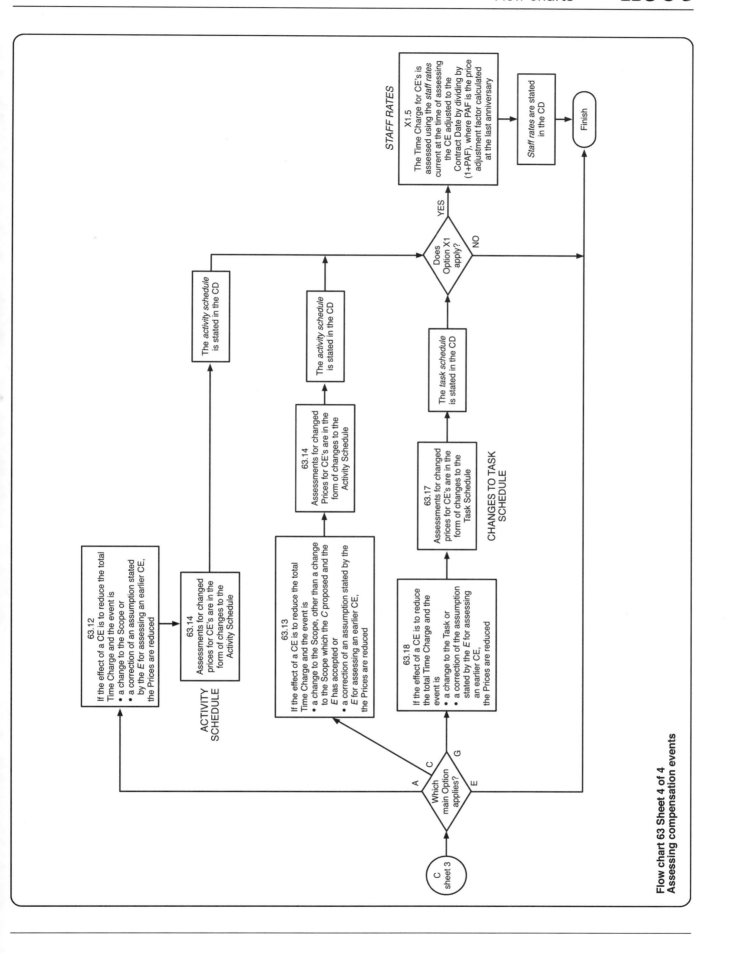

Flow chart 63 Sheet 4 of 4
Assessing compensation events

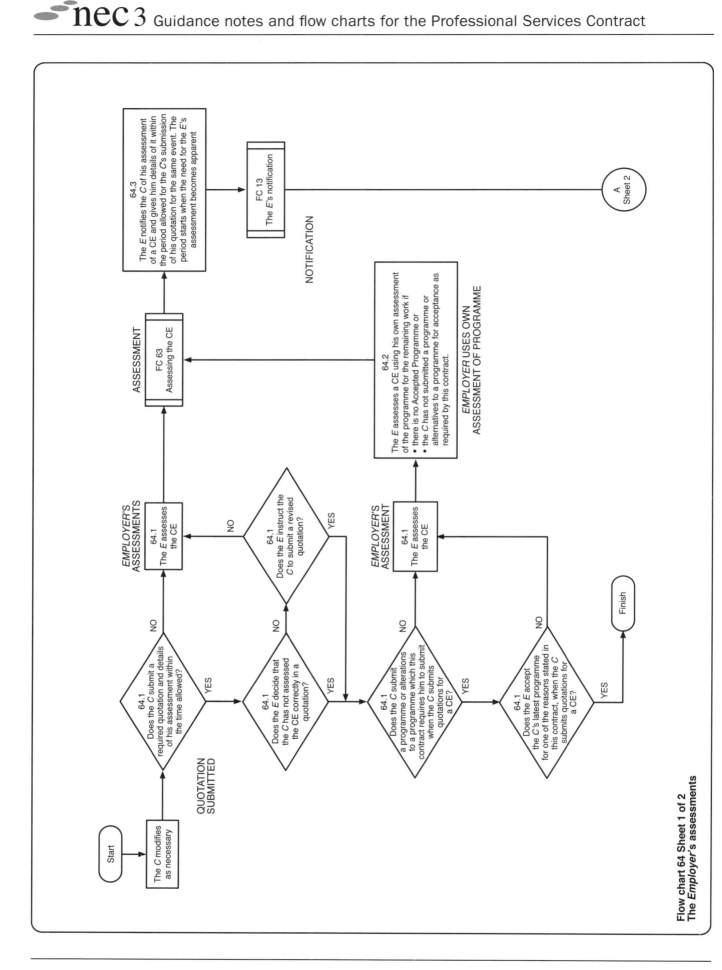

Flow chart 64 Sheet 1 of 2
The *Employer's* assessments

nec 3

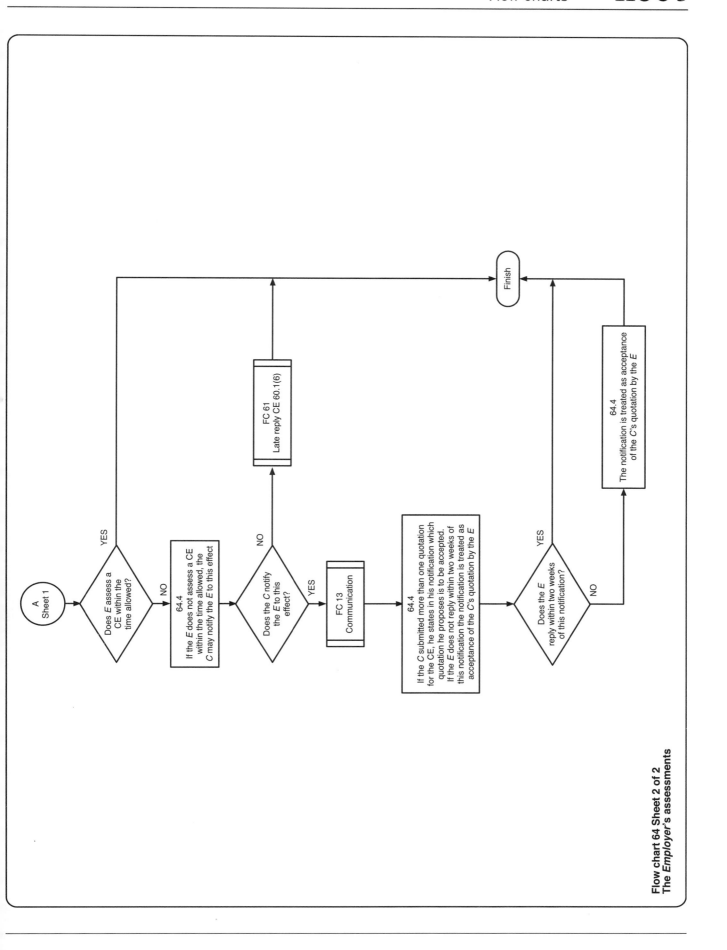

A Sheet 1

Does E assess a CE within the time allowed?

YES

NO

64.4
If the E does not assess a CE within the time allowed, the C may notify the E to this effect

Does the C notify the E to this effect?

NO

YES

FC 61
Late reply CE 60.1(6)

FC 13
Communication

64.4
If the C submitted more than one quotation for the CE, he states in his notification which quotation he proposes is to be accepted.
If the E does not reply within two weeks of this notification the notification is treated as acceptance of the C's quotation by the E

Does the E reply within two weeks of this notification?

YES

NO

64.4
The notification is treated as acceptance of the C's quotation by the E

Finish

Flow chart 64 Sheet 2 of 2
The *Employer*'s assessments

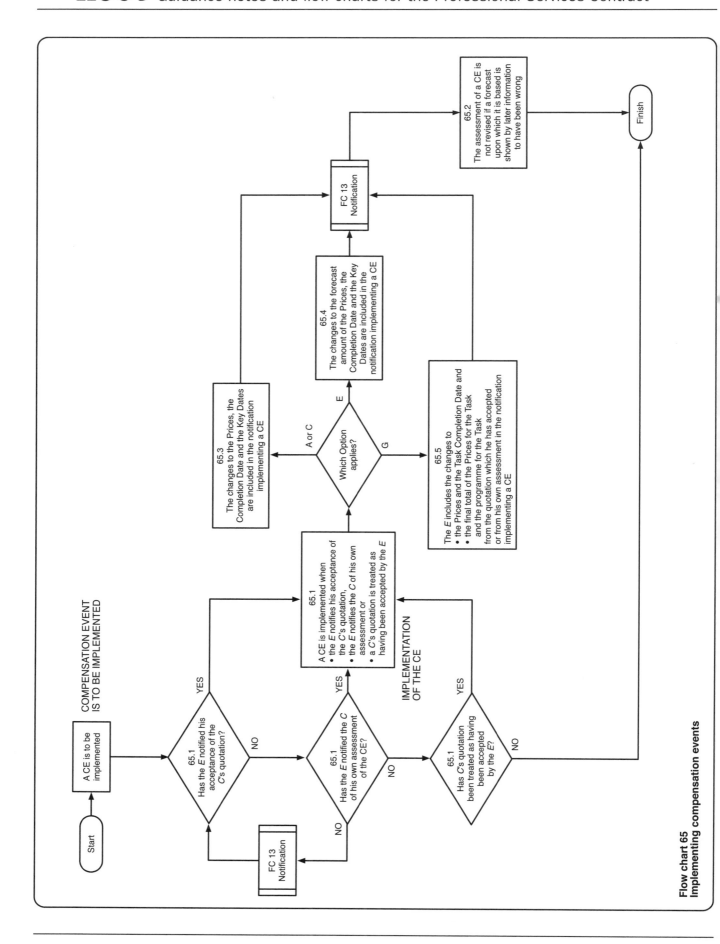

COMPENSATION EVENT
IS TO BE IMPLEMENTED

Start

A CE is to be
implemented

65.1
Has the *E* notified his
acceptance of the
C's quotation?

YES

NO

FC 13
Notification

65.1
Has the *E* notified the *C*
of his own assessment
of the CE?

YES

NO

65.1
A CE is implemented when
• the *E* notifies his acceptance of
the *C*'s quotation,
• the *E* notifies the *C* of his own
assessment or
• a *C*'s quotation is treated as
having been accepted by the *E*

IMPLEMENTATION
OF THE CE

65.1
Has *C*'s quotation
been treated as having
been accepted
by the *E*?

YES

NO

Which Option
applies?

A or C

E

G

65.3
The changes to the Prices, the
Completion Date and the Key Dates
are included in the notification
implementing a CE

65.4
The changes to the forecast
amount of the Prices, the
Completion Date and the Key
Dates are included in the
notification implementing a CE

65.5
The *E* includes the changes to
• the Prices and the Task Completion Date and
• the final total of the Prices for the Task
and the programme for the Task
from the quotation which he has accepted
or from his own assessment in the notification
implementing a CE

FC 13
Notification

65.2
The assessment of a CE is
not revised if a forecast
upon which it is based is
shown by later information
to have been wrong

Finish

Flow chart 65
Implementing compensation events

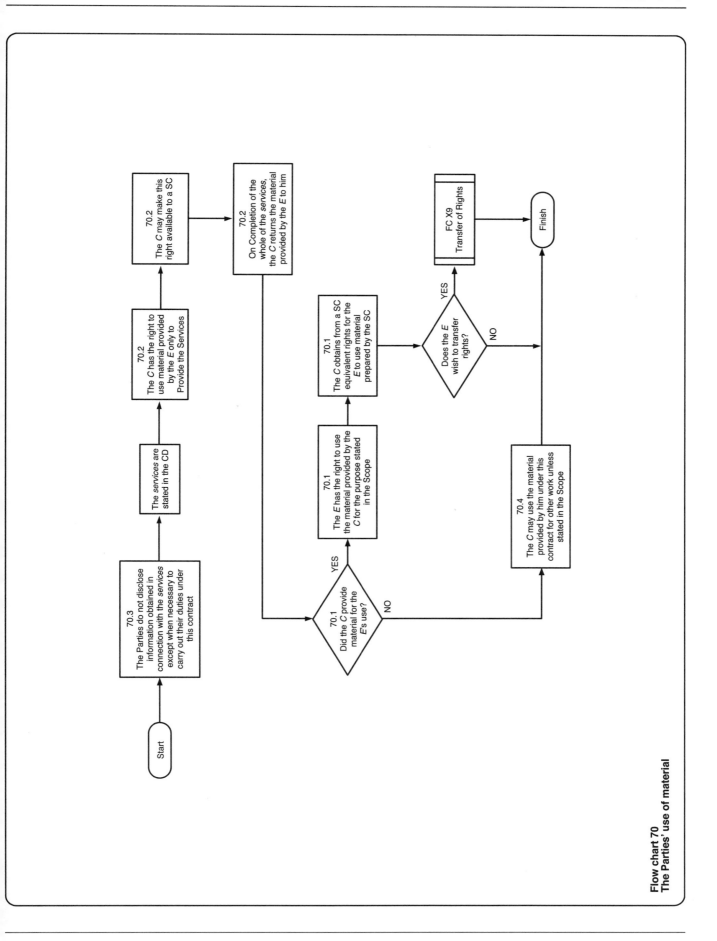

Flow chart 70
The Parties' use of material

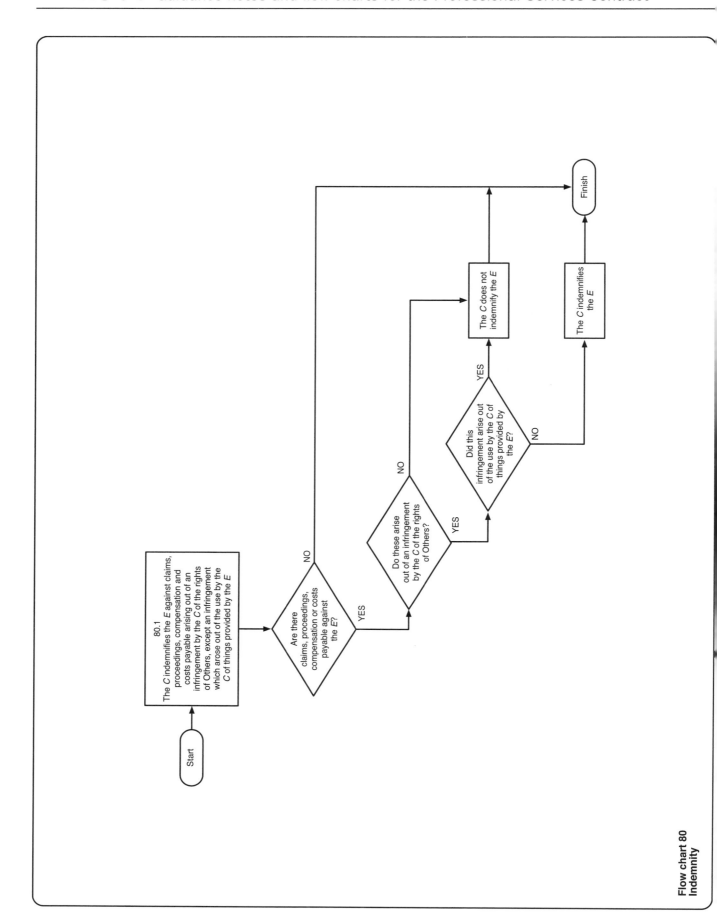

Start

80.1
The *C* indemnifies the *E* against claims, proceedings, compensation and costs payable arising out of an infringement by the *C* of the rights of Others, except an infringement which arose out of the use by the *C* of things provided by the *E*

Are there claims, proceedings, compensation or costs payable against the *E*?

NO → Finish

YES →

Do these arise out of an infringement by the *C* of the rights of Others?

NO → The *C* does not indemnify the *E*

YES →

Did this infringement arise out of the use by the *C* of things provided by the *E*?

YES → The *C* does not indemnify the *E*

NO → The *C* indemnifies the *E* → Finish

Flow chart 80
Indemnity

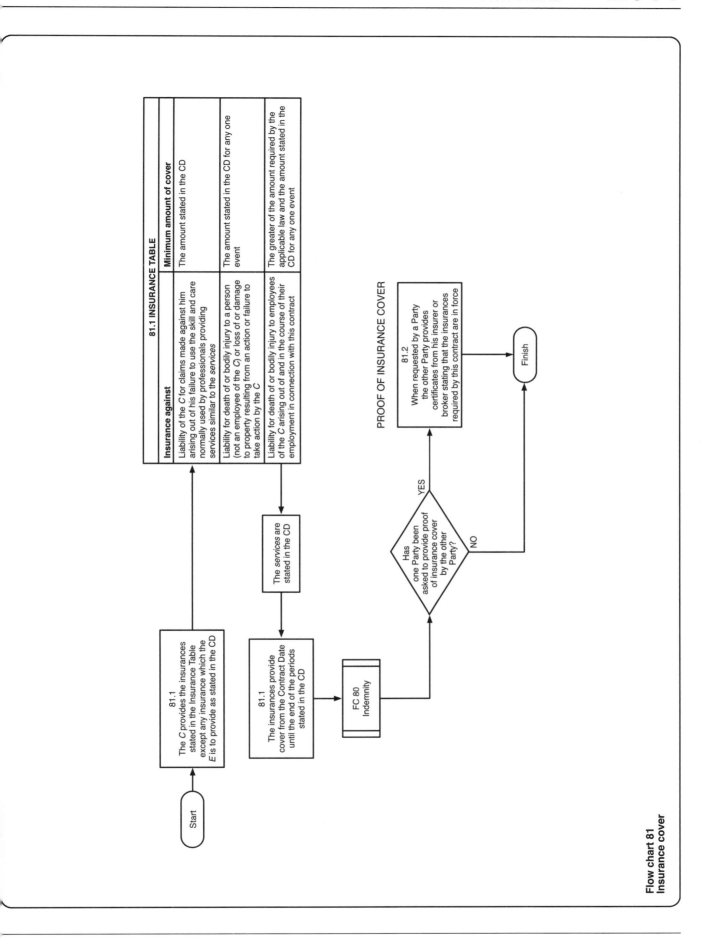

81.1 INSURANCE TABLE

Insurance against	Minimum amount of cover
Liability of the *C* for claims made against him arising out of his failure to use the skill and care normally used by professionals providing services similar to the *services*	The amount stated in the CD
Liability for death of or bodily injury to a person (not an employee of the *C*) or loss of or damage to property resulting from an action or failure to take action by the *C*	The amount stated in the CD for any one event
Liability for death of or bodily injury to employees of the *C* arising out of and in the course of their employment in connection with this contract	The greater of the amount required by the applicable law and the amount stated in the CD for any one event

PROOF OF INSURANCE COVER

81.2
When requested by a Party the other Party provides certificates from his insurer or broker stating that the insurances required by this contract are in force

Finish

Has one Party been asked to provide proof of insurance cover by the other Party? — YES / NO

81.1
The *C* provides the insurances stated in the Insurance Table except any insurance which the *E* is to provide as stated in the CD

The *services* are stated in the CD

81.1
The insurances provide cover from the Contract Date until the end of the periods stated in the CD

FC 80 Indemnity

Start

Flow chart 81 Insurance cover

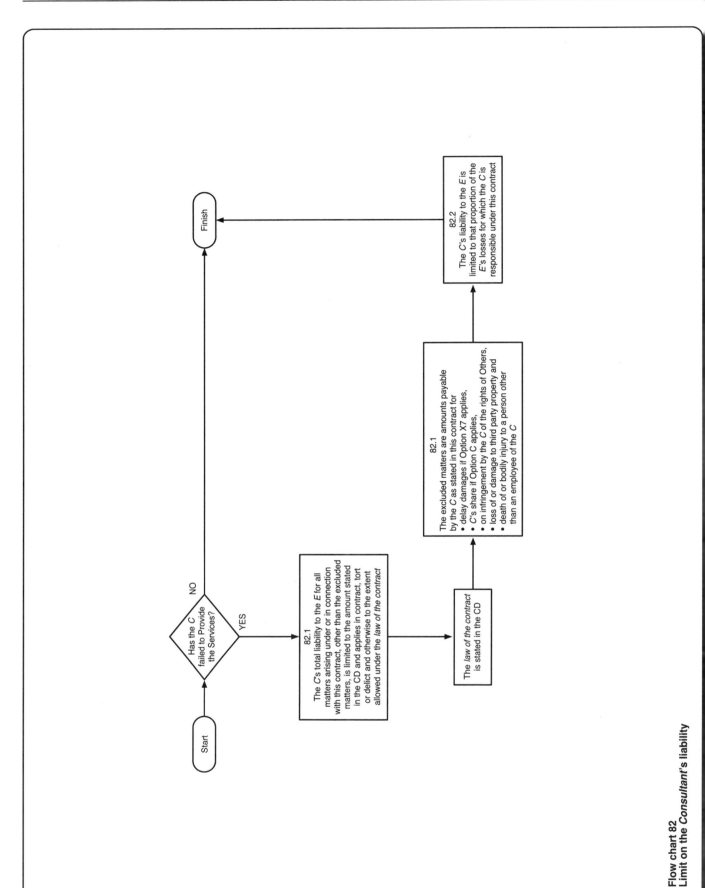

Start

Has the C failed to Provide the Services?

NO → **Finish**

YES

82.1
The C's total liability to the E for all matters arising under or in connection with this contract, other than the excluded matters, is limited to the amount stated in the CD and applies in contract, tort or delict and otherwise to the extent allowed under the *law of the contract*

↓

The *law of the contract* is stated in the CD

↓

82.1
The excluded matters are amounts payable by the C as stated in this contract for
• delay damages if Option X7 applies,
• C's share if Option C applies,
• on infringement by the C of the rights of Others,
• loss of or damage to third party property and
• death of or bodily injury to a person other than an employee of the C

↓

82.2
The C's liability to the E is limited to that proportion of the E's losses for which the C is responsible under this contract

→ **Finish**

Flow chart 82
Limit on the *Consultant's* liability

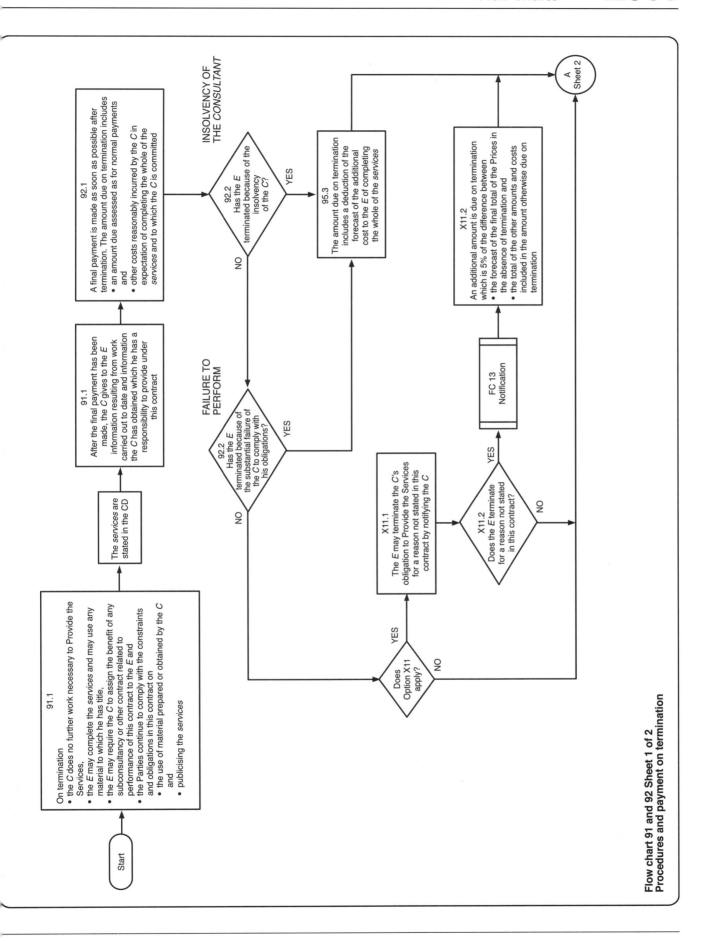

Start

91.1

On termination
- the *C* does no further work necessary to Provide the Services,
- the *E* may complete the *services* and may use any material to which he has title,
- the *E* may require the *C* to assign the benefit of any subconsultancy or other contract related to performance of this contract to the *E* and
- the Parties continue to comply with the constraints and obligations in this contract on
  - the use of material prepared or obtained by the *C* and
  - publicising the *services*

The *services* are stated in the CD

91.1

After the final payment has been made, the *C* gives to the *E* information resulting from work carried out to date and information the *C* has obtained which he has a responsibility to provide under this contract

92.1

A final payment is made as soon as possible after termination. The amount due on termination includes
- an amount due assessed as for normal payments and
- other costs reasonably incurred by the *C* in expectation of completing the whole of the *services* and to which the *C* is committed

INSOLVENCY OF THE CONSULTANT

92.2
Has the *E* terminated because of the insolvency of the *C*?

NO / YES

FAILURE TO PERFORM

92.2
Has the *E* terminated because of the substantial failure of the *C* to comply with his obligations?

NO / YES

95.3

The amount due on termination includes a deduction of the forecast of the additional cost to the *E* of completing the whole of the *services*

X11.1

The *E* may terminate the *C*'s obligation to Provide the Services for a reason not stated in this contract by notifying the *C*

X11.2
Does the *E* terminate for a reason not stated in this contract?

YES / NO

Does Option X11 apply?

YES / NO

FC 13
Notification

X11.2

An additional amount is due on termination which is 5% of the difference between
- the forecast of the final total of the Prices in the absence of termination and
- the total of the other amounts and costs included in the amount otherwise due on termination

A
Sheet 2

**Flow chart 91 and 92 Sheet 1 of 2
Procedures and payment on termination**

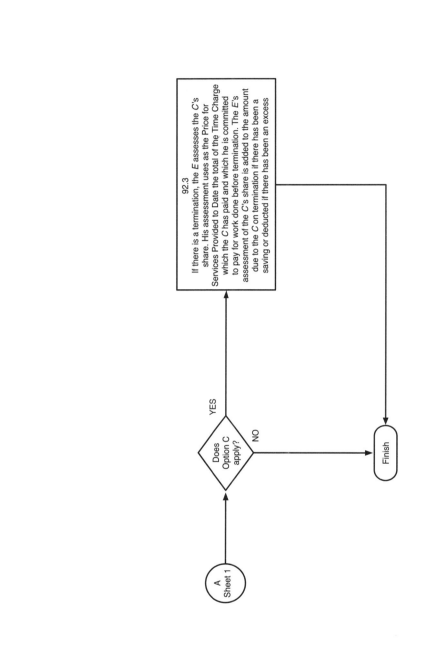

92.3

If there is a termination, the *E* assesses the *C*'s share. His assessment uses as the Price for Services Provided to Date the total of the Time Charge which the *C* has paid and which he is committed to pay for work done before termination. The *E*'s assessment of the *C*'s share is added to the amount due to the *C* on termination if there has been a saving or deducted if there has been an excess

YES

Does Option C apply?

NO

Finish

A Sheet 1

Flow chart 91 and 92 Sheet 2 of 2
Procedures and payment on termination

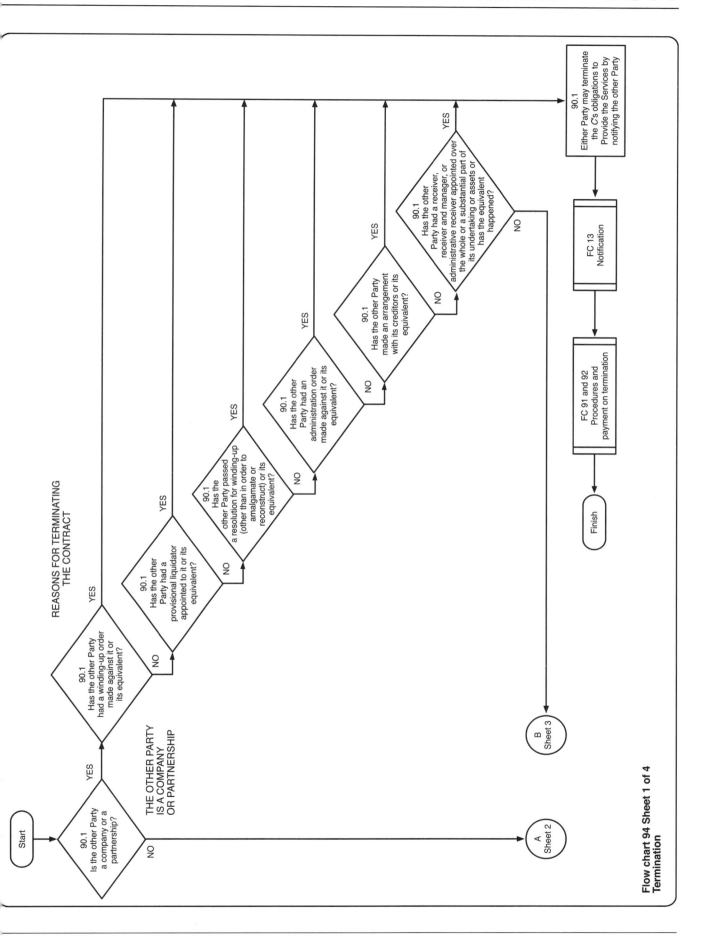

Flow chart 94 Sheet 1 of 4
Termination

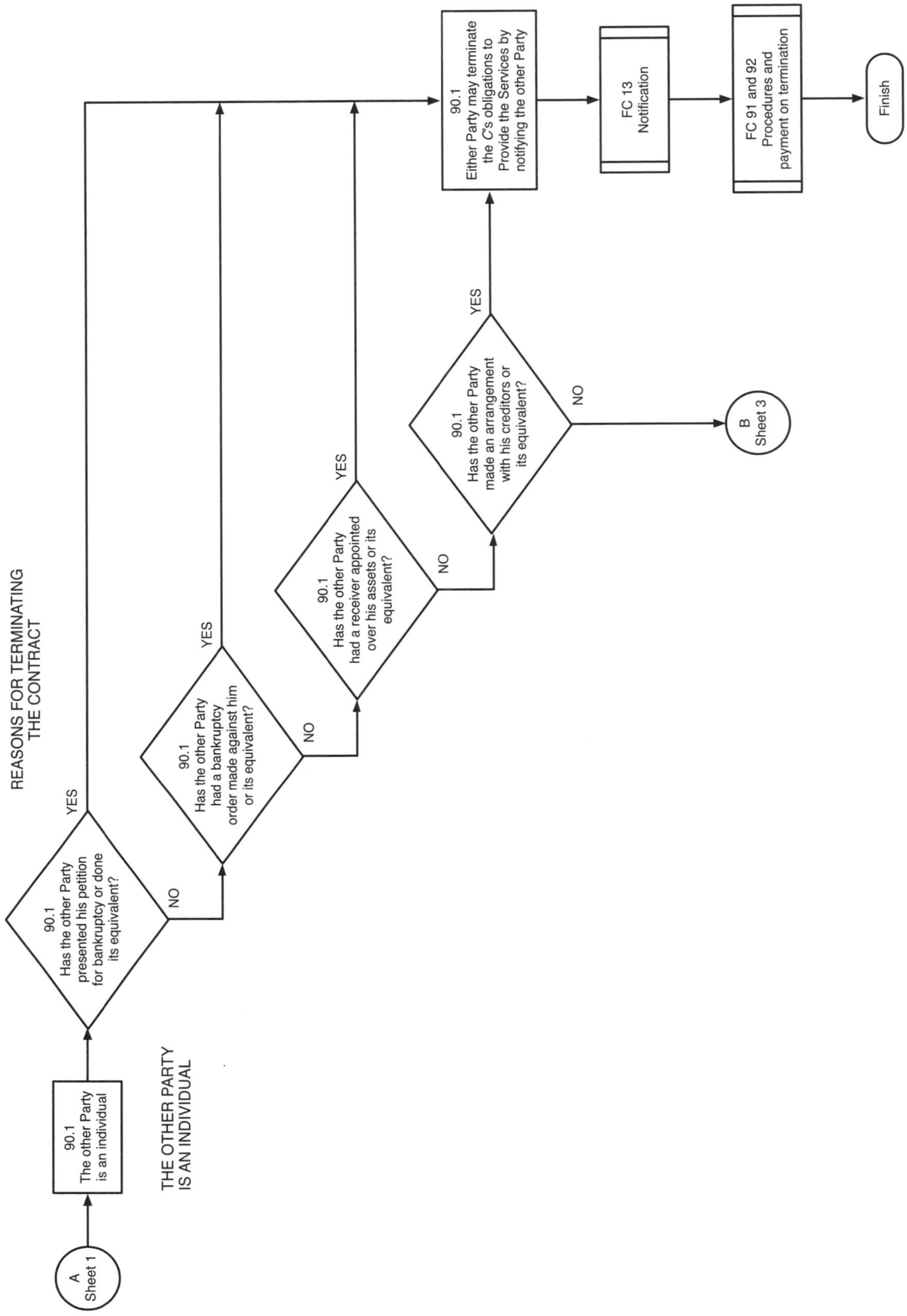
A Sheet 1
90.1 The other Party is an individual
THE OTHER PARTY IS AN INDIVIDUAL
REASONS FOR TERMINATING THE CONTRACT
90.1 Has the other Party presented his petition for bankruptcy or done its equivalent?
YES
NO
90.1 Has the other Party had a bankruptcy order made against him or its equivalent?
YES
NO
90.1 Has the other Party had a receiver appointed over his assets or its equivalent?
YES
NO
90.1 Has the other Party made an arrangement with his creditors or its equivalent?
YES
NO
B Sheet 3
90.1 Either Party may terminate the C's obligations to Provide the Services by notifying the other Party
FC 13 Notification
FC 91 and 92 Procedures and payment on termination
Finish

Flow chart 94 Sheet 2 of 4
Termination

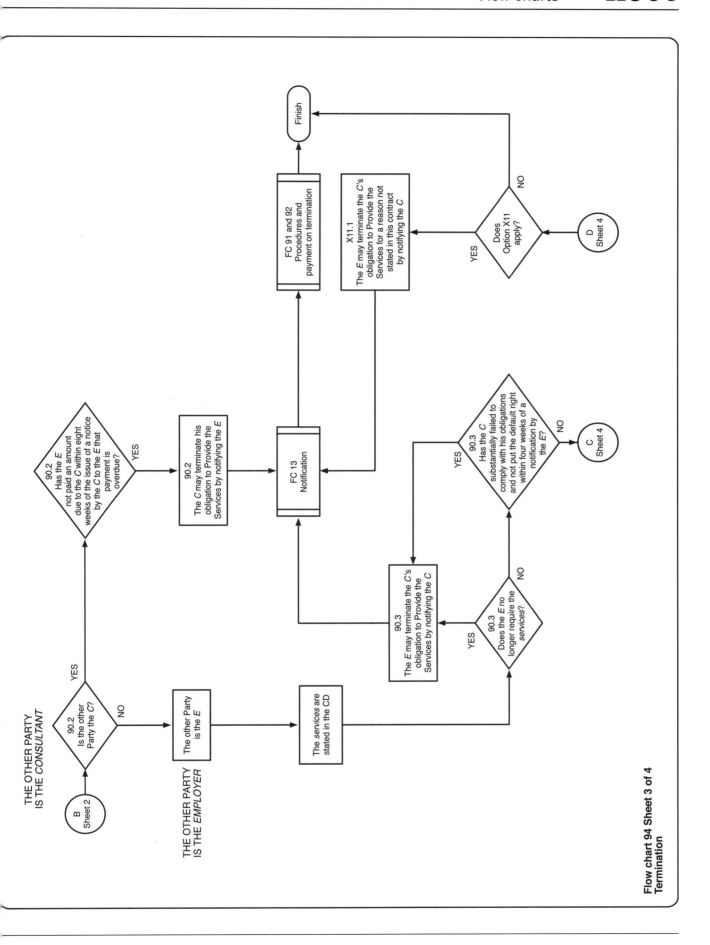

THE OTHER PARTY IS THE *CONSULTANT*

THE OTHER PARTY IS THE *EMPLOYER*

B
Sheet 2

90.2
Is the other
Party the *C*?

YES

NO

The other Party
is the *E*

The *services* are
stated in the CD

90.2
Has the *E*
not paid an amount
due to the *C* within eight
weeks of the issue of a notice
by the *C* to the *E* that
payment is
overdue?

YES

90.2
The *C* may terminate his
obligation to Provide the
Services by notifying the *E*

FC 13
Notification

FC 91 and 92
Procedures and
payment on termination

Finish

X11.1
The *E* may terminate the *C*'s
obligation to Provide the
Services for a reason not
stated in this contract
by notifying the *C*

Does
Option X11
apply?

YES

NO

D
Sheet 4

90.3
The *E* may terminate the *C*'s
obligation to Provide the
Services by notifying the *C*

90.3
Has the *C*
substantially failed to
comply with his obligations
and not put the default right
within four weeks of a
notification by
the *E*?

YES

NO

C
Sheet 4

90.3
Does the *E* no
longer require the
services?

YES

NO

**Flow chart 94 Sheet 3 of 4
Termination**

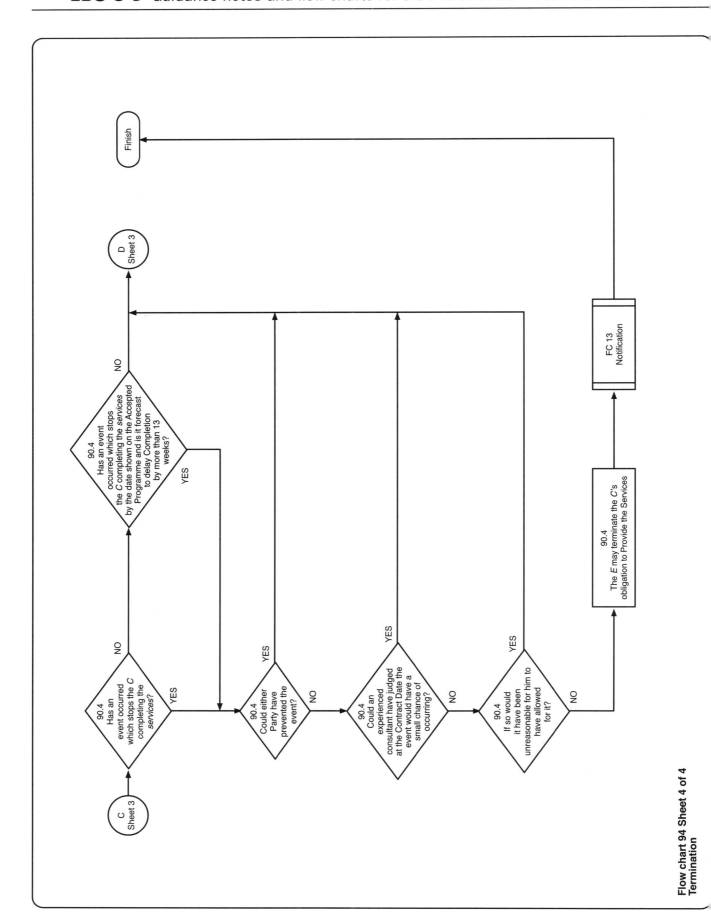

Flow chart 94 Sheet 4 of 4
Termination

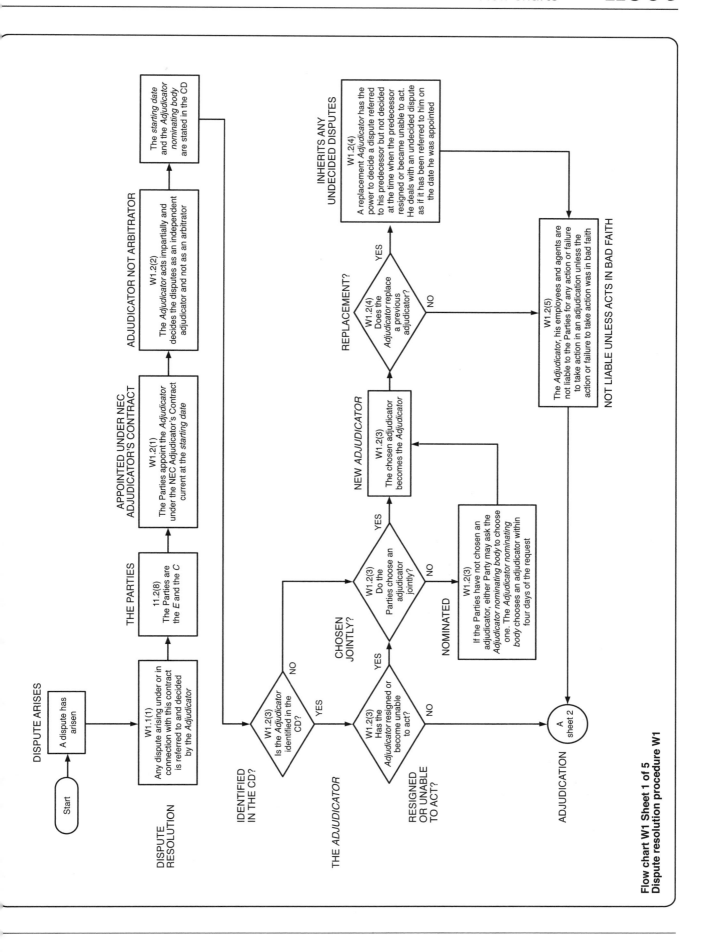

DISPUTE ARISES

Start

A dispute has arisen

DISPUTE RESOLUTION

W1.1(1)
Any dispute arising under or in connection with this contract is referred to and decided by the *Adjudicator*

THE PARTIES

11.2(8)
The Parties are the *E* and the *C*

APPOINTED UNDER NEC ADJUDICATOR'S CONTRACT

W1.2(1)
The Parties appoint the *Adjudicator* under the NEC Adjudicator's Contract current at the *starting date*

ADJUDICATOR NOT ARBITRATOR

W1.2(2)
The *Adjudicator* acts impartially and decides the disputes as an independent adjudicator and not as an arbitrator

The *starting date* and the *Adjudicator nominating body* are stated in the CD

IDENTIFIED IN THE CD?

W1.2(3)
Is the *Adjudicator* identified in the CD?

NO / YES

THE *ADJUDICATOR*

W1.2(3)
Has the *Adjudicator* resigned or become unable to act?

RESIGNED OR UNABLE TO ACT?

YES / NO

CHOSEN JOINTLY?

W1.2(3)
Do the Parties choose an adjudicator jointly?

YES / NO

NOMINATED

W1.2(3)
If the Parties have not chosen an adjudicator, either Party may ask the *Adjudicator nominating body* to choose one. The *Adjudicator nominating body* chooses an adjudicator within four days of the request

NEW *ADJUDICATOR*

W1.2(3)
The chosen adjudicator becomes the *Adjudicator*

REPLACEMENT?

W1.2(4)
Does the *Adjudicator* replace a previous adjudicator?

YES / NO

INHERITS ANY UNDECIDED DISPUTES

W1.2(4)
A replacement *Adjudicator* has the power to decide a dispute referred to his predecessor but not decided at the time when the predecessor resigned or became unable to act. He deals with an undecided dispute as if it has been referred to him on the date he was appointed

W1.2(5)
The *Adjudicator*, his employees and agents are not liable to the Parties for any action or failure to take action in an adjudication unless the action or failure to take action was in bad faith

NOT LIABLE UNLESS ACTS IN BAD FAITH

ADJUDICATION

A
sheet 2

Flow chart W1 Sheet 1 of 5
Dispute resolution procedure W1

ADJUDICATION TABLE

Dispute about:	Which Party may refer it to the *Adjudicator*?	When may it be referred to the *Adjudicator*?
An action of the *E*	The *C*	Between two and four weeks after the *C*'s notification of the dispute to the *E*, the notification itself being made not more than four weeks after the *C* becomes aware of the action
The *E* not having taken an action	The *C*	Between two and four weeks after the *C*'s notification of the dispute to the *E*, the notification itself being made not more than four weeks after the *C* becomes aware that the action was not taken
A quotation for a CE which is treated as having been accepted	The *E*	Between two and four weeks after the *E*'s notification of the dispute to the *C*, the notification itself being made not more than four weeks after the quotation was treated as accepted
Any other matter	Either Party	Between two and four weeks after notification of the dispute to the other Party

ADJUDICATION

A sheet 1

THE ADJUDICATION

W1.3(1)
Disputes are notified and referred to the *Adjudicator* in accordance with the Adjudication Table

EXTENSION?

W1.3(2)
Do the *C* and the *E* agree to an extension before notice or referral is due?

NO / YES

EXTENSION AGREED

W1.3(2)
The times for notifying and referring a dispute may be extended if the *C* and the *E* agree to the extension before the notice or referral is due

NOTIFIED AND REFERRED IN TIME?

W1.3(2)
Is the disputed matter notified and referred within the times set out in this contract?

NO / YES

NOT ADJUDICABLE

W1.3(2)
If a disputed matter is not notified and referred within the times set out in this contract, neither Party may subsequently refer it to the *Adjudicator* or the *tribunal*

NOTIFICATION

FC 13
Notification

INFORMATION WITH SUBMISSION

W1.3(3)
The Party referring the dispute to the *Adjudicator* includes with his referral information to be considered by the *Adjudicator*

MORE INFORMATION

W1.3(3)
Any more information from a Party to be considered by the *Adjudicator* is provided within four weeks of the referral

ADDITIONAL TIME

W1.3(3)
This period may be extended if the *Adjudicator* and the Parties agree

COMMUNICATIONS SHARED

W1.3(6)
Any communication between a Party and the *Adjudicator* is communicated to the other Party at the same time

ADJUDICATION (CONTINUED)

A sheet 3

Finish

Flow chart W1 Sheet 2 of 5
Dispute resolution procedure W1

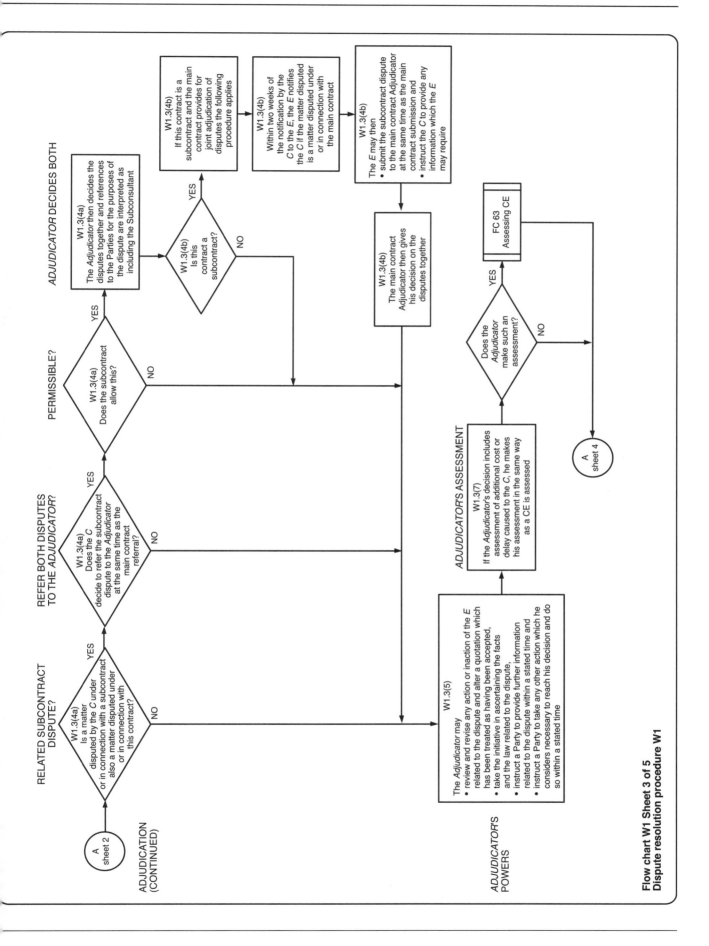

Flow chart W1 Sheet 3 of 5
Dispute resolution procedure W1

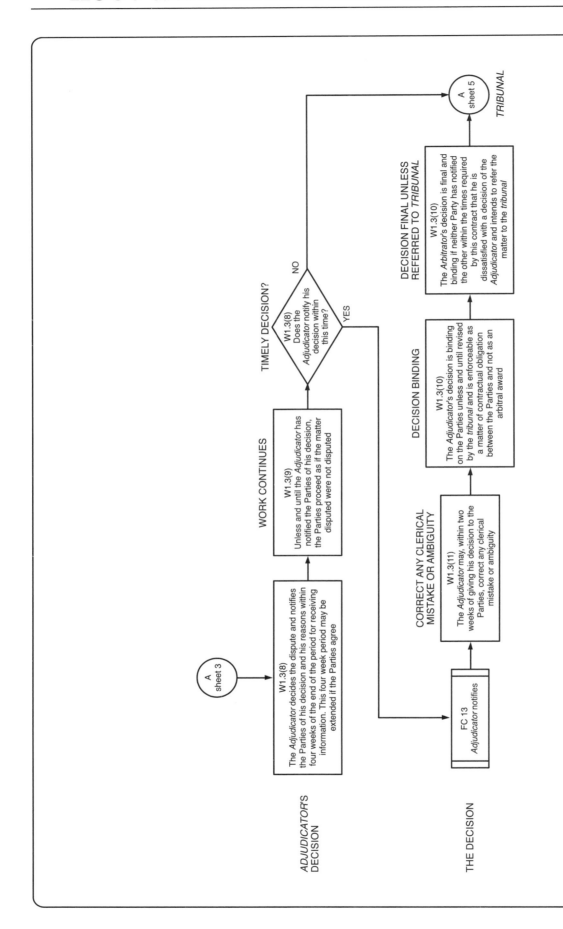

ADJUDICATOR'S DECISION

WORK CONTINUES

TIMELY DECISION?

W1.3(8)
The *Adjudicator* decides the dispute and notifies the Parties of his decision and his reasons within four weeks of the end of the period for receiving information. This four week period may be extended if the Parties agree

W1.3(9)
Unless and until the *Adjudicator* has notified the Parties of his decision, the Parties proceed as if the matter disputed were not disputed

W1.3(8)
Does the *Adjudicator* notify his decision within this time?

NO

YES

A
sheet 3

A
sheet 5

TRIBUNAL

DECISION FINAL UNLESS REFERRED TO *TRIBUNAL*

W1.3(10)
The *Arbitrator's* decision is final and binding if neither Party has notified the other within the times required by this contract that he is dissatisfied with a decision of the *Adjudicator* and intends to refer the matter to the *tribunal*

DECISION BINDING

W1.3(10)
The *Adjudicator's* decision is binding on the Parties unless and until revised by the *tribunal* and is enforceable as a matter of contractual obligation between the Parties and not as an arbitral award

CORRECT ANY CLERICAL MISTAKE OR AMBIGUITY

W1.3(11)
The *Adjudicator* may, within two weeks of giving his decision to the Parties, correct any clerical mistake or ambiguity

FC 13
Adjudicator notifies

THE DECISION

Flow chart W1 Sheet 4 of 5
Dispute resolution procedure W1

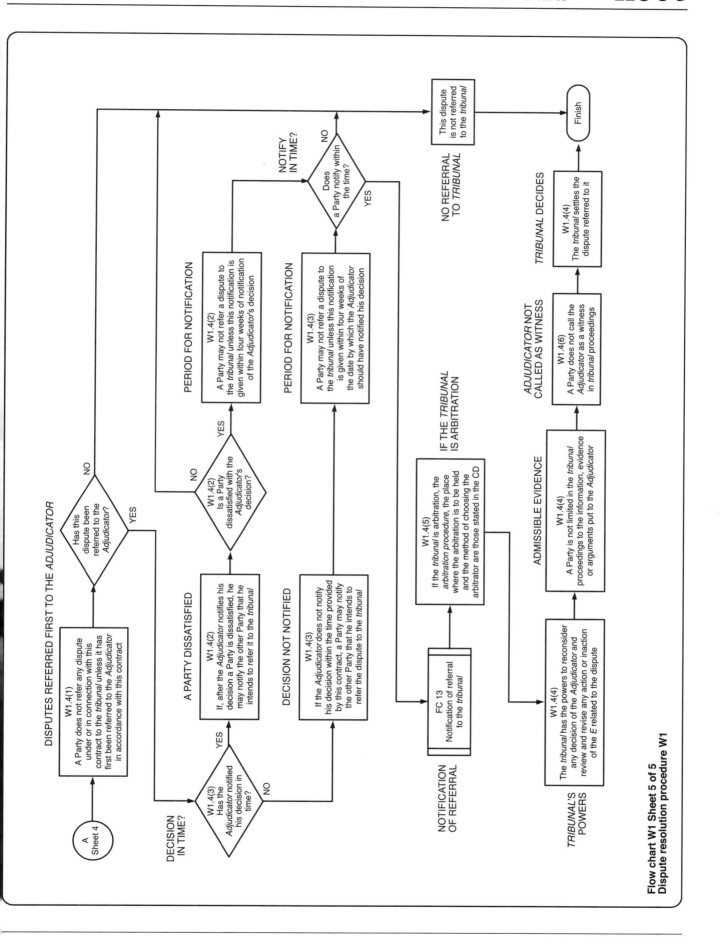

DISPUTES REFERRED FIRST TO THE *ADJUDICATOR*

W1.4(1)
A Party does not refer any dispute under or in connection with this contract to the *tribunal* unless it has first been referred to the *Adjudicator* in accordance with this contract

Has this dispute been referred to the *Adjudicator*?

NO / YES

DECISION IN TIME?
W1.4(3)
Has the *Adjudicator* notified his decision in time?

YES / NO

A PARTY DISSATISFIED
W1.4(2)
If, after the *Adjudicator* notifies his decision a Party is dissatisfied, he may notify the other Party that he intends to refer it to the *tribunal*

W1.4(2)
Is a Party dissatisfied with the *Adjudicator's* decision?

YES / NO

PERIOD FOR NOTIFICATION
W1.4(2)
A Party may not refer a dispute to the *tribunal* unless this notification is given within four weeks of notification of the *Adjudicator's* decision

DECISION NOT NOTIFIED
W1.4(3)
If the *Adjudicator* does not notify his decision within the time provided by this contract, a Party may notify the other Party that he intends to refer the dispute to the *tribunal*

PERIOD FOR NOTIFICATION
W1.4(3)
A Party may not refer a dispute to the *tribunal* unless this notification is given within four weeks of the date by which the *Adjudicator* should have notified his decision

NOTIFY IN TIME?
Does a Party notify within the time?

NO / YES

This dispute is not referred to the *tribunal*

NO REFERRAL TO *TRIBUNAL*

NOTIFICATION OF REFERRAL
FC 13
Notification of referral to the *tribunal*

IF THE *TRIBUNAL* IS ARBITRATION
W1.4(5)
If the *tribunal* is arbitration, the *arbitration procedure*, the place where the arbitration is to be held and the method of choosing the arbitrator are those stated in the CD

TRIBUNAL'S POWERS
W1.4(4)
The *tribunal* has the powers to reconsider any decision of the *Adjudicator* and review and revise any action or inaction of the *E* related to the dispute

ADMISSIBLE EVIDENCE
W1.4(4)
A Party is not limited in the *tribunal* proceedings to the information, evidence or arguments put to the *Adjudicator*

ADJUDICATOR NOT CALLED AS WITNESS
W1.4(6)
A Party does not call the *Adjudicator* as a witness in *tribunal* proceedings

TRIBUNAL DECIDES
W1.4(4)
The *tribunal* settles the dispute referred to it

Finish

A Sheet 4

Flow chart W1 Sheet 5 of 5
Dispute resolution procedure W1

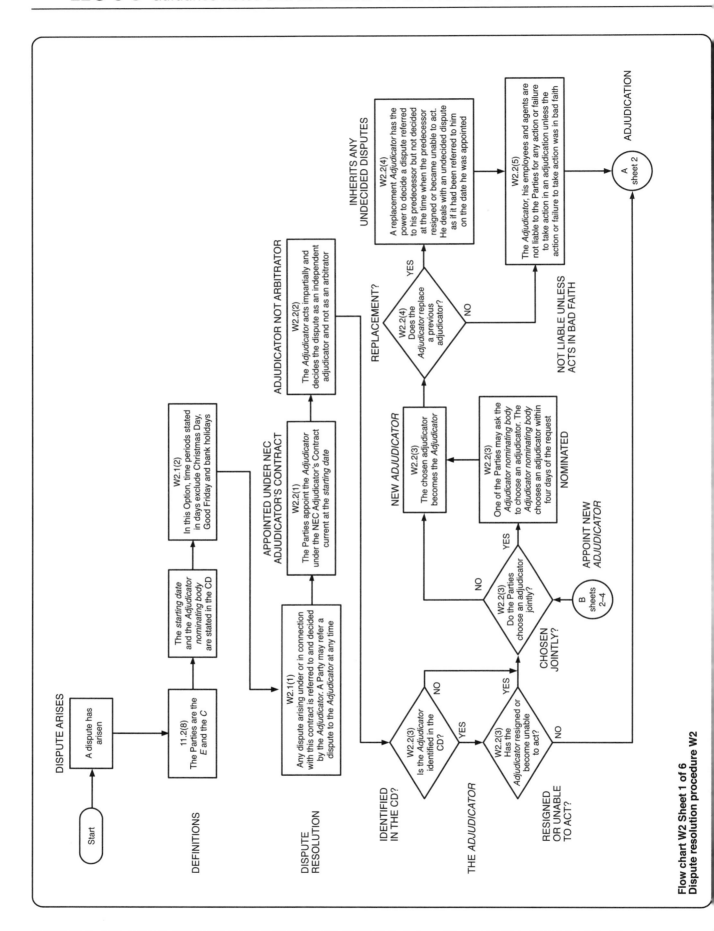

DISPUTE ARISES

A dispute has arisen

Start

DEFINITIONS

11.2(8)
The Parties are the *E* and the *C*

W2.1(2)
In this Option, time periods stated in days exclude Christmas Day, Good Friday and bank holidays

The *starting date* and the *Adjudicator nominating body* are stated in the CD

DISPUTE RESOLUTION

W2.1(1)
Any dispute arising under or in connection with this contract is referred to and decided by the *Adjudicator*. A Party may refer a dispute to the *Adjudicator* at any time

APPOINTED UNDER NEC ADJUDICATOR'S CONTRACT

W2.2(1)
The Parties appoint the *Adjudicator* under the NEC Adjudicator's Contract current at the *starting date*

ADJUDICATOR NOT ARBITRATOR

W2.2(2)
The *Adjudicator* acts impartially and decides the dispute as an independent adjudicator and not as an arbitrator

IDENTIFIED IN THE CD?

W2.2(3)
Is the *Adjudicator* identified in the CD?

NO

YES

THE ADJUDICATOR

W2.2(3)
Has the *Adjudicator* resigned or become unable to act?

YES

NO

RESIGNED OR UNABLE TO ACT?

CHOSEN JOINTLY?

W2.2(3)
Do the Parties choose an adjudicator jointly?

YES

NO

B
sheets 2–4

APPOINT NEW ADJUDICATOR

NOMINATED

W2.2(3)
One of the Parties may ask the *Adjudicator nominating body* to choose an adjudicator. The *Adjudicator nominating body* chooses an adjudicator within four days of the request

NEW ADJUDICATOR

W2.2(3)
The chosen adjudicator becomes the *Adjudicator*

REPLACEMENT?

W2.2(4)
Does the *Adjudicator* replace a previous adjudicator?

YES

NO

INHERITS ANY UNDECIDED DISPUTES

W2.2(4)
A replacement *Adjudicator* has the power to decide a dispute referred to his predecessor but not decided at the time when the predecessor resigned or became unable to act. He deals with an undecided dispute as if it had been referred to him on the date he was appointed

W2.2(5)
The *Adjudicator*, his employees and agents are not liable to the Parties for any action or failure to take action in an adjudication unless the action or failure to take action was in bad faith

NOT LIABLE UNLESS ACTS IN BAD FAITH

A
sheet 2

ADJUDICATION

Flow chart W2 Sheet 1 of 6
Dispute resolution procedure W2

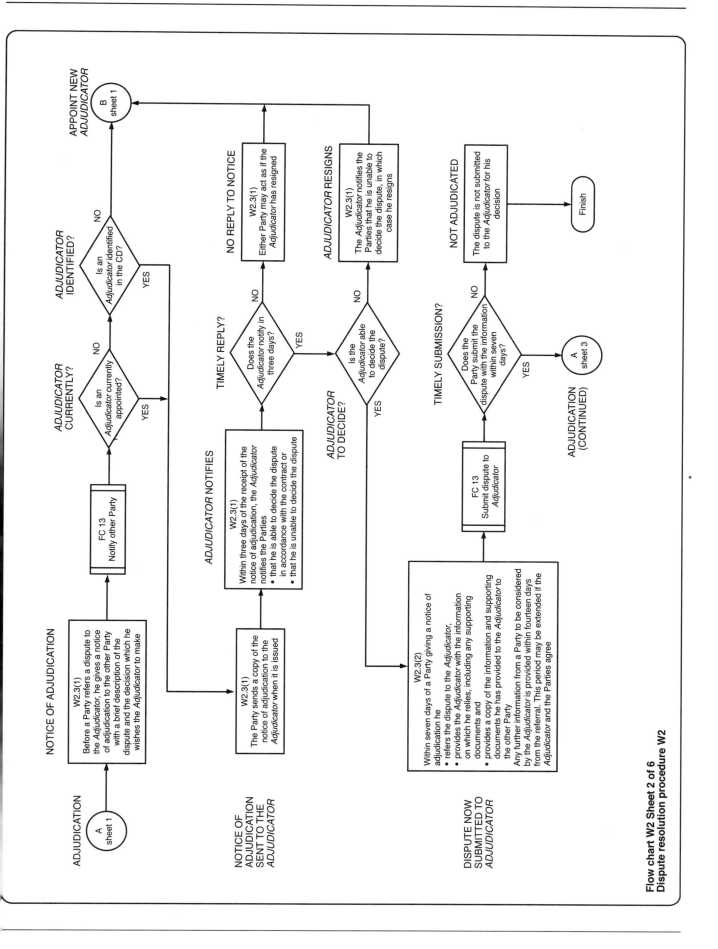

Flow chart W2 Sheet 2 of 6
Dispute resolution procedure W2

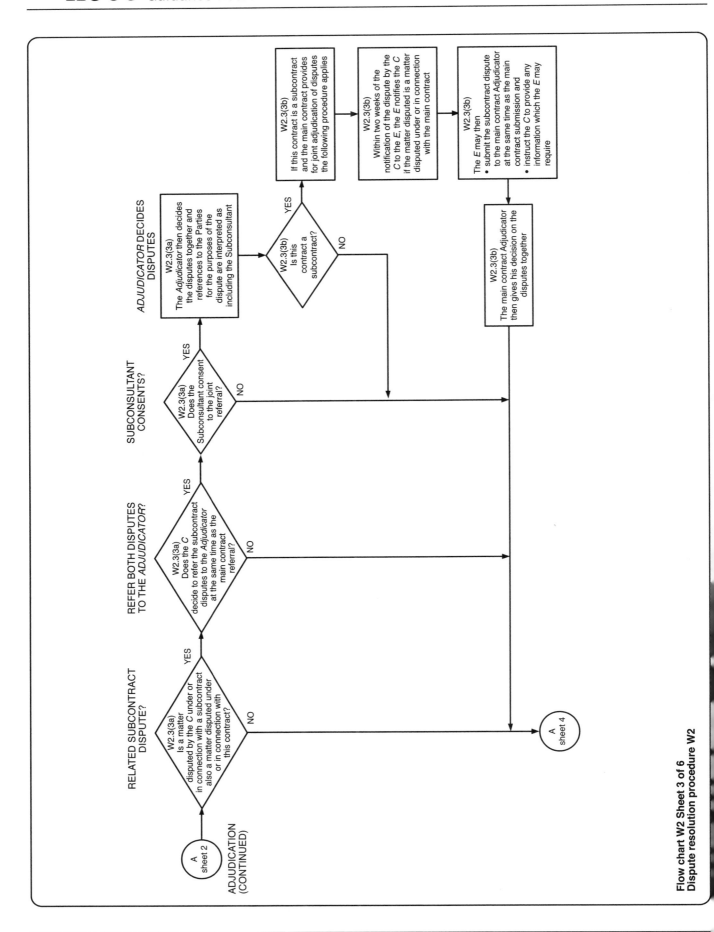

RELATED SUBCONTRACT DISPUTE?

REFER BOTH DISPUTES TO THE ADJUDICATOR?

SUBCONSULTANT CONSENTS?

ADJUDICATOR DECIDES DISPUTES

A sheet 2

ADJUDICATION (CONTINUED)

W2.3(3a) Is a matter disputed by the C under or in connection with a subcontract also a matter disputed under or in connection with this contract?

W2.3(3a) Does the C decide to refer the subcontract disputes to the Adjudicator at the same time as the main contract referral?

W2.3(3a) Does the Subconsultant consent to the joint referral?

W2.3(3a) The Adjudicator then decides the disputes together and references to the Parties for the purposes of the dispute are interpreted as including the Subconsultant

W2.3(3b) Is this contract a subcontract?

W2.3(3b) If this contract is a subcontract and the main contract provides for joint adjudication of disputes the following procedure applies

W2.3(3b) Within two weeks of the notification of the dispute by the C to the E, the E notifies the C if the matter disputed is a matter disputed under or in connection with the main contract

W2.3(3b) The E may then
• submit the subcontract dispute to the main contract Adjudicator at the same time as the main contract submission and
• instruct the C to provide any information which the E may require

W2.3(3b) The main contract Adjudicator then gives his decision on the disputes together

A sheet 4

Flow chart W2 Sheet 3 of 6
Dispute resolution procedure W2

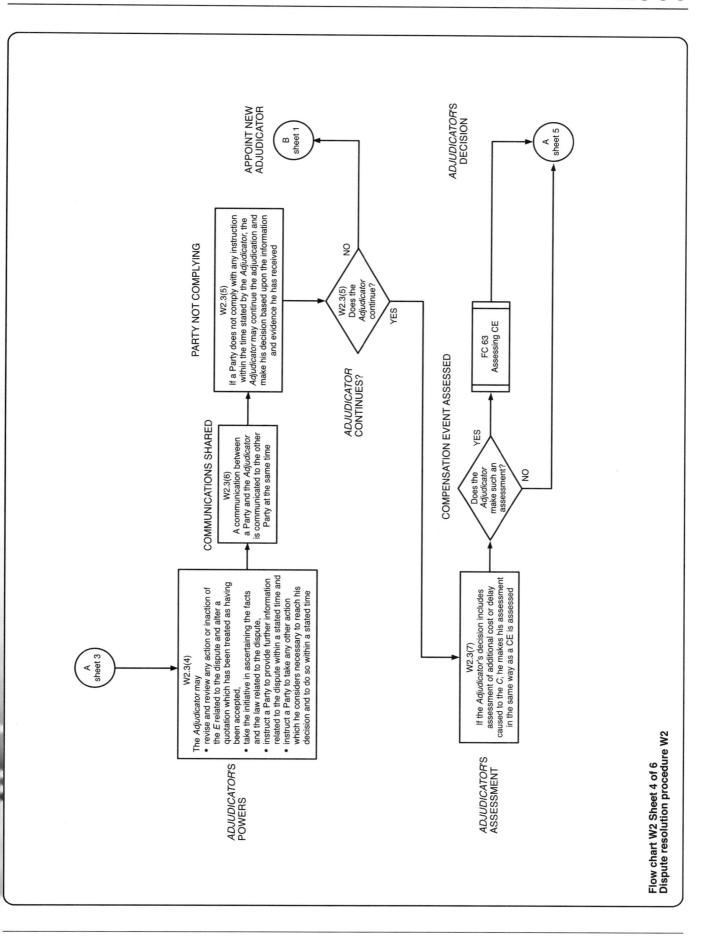

ADJUDICATOR'S POWERS

A sheet 3

W2.3(4)
The *Adjudicator* may
- revise and review any action or inaction of the *Employer* related to the dispute and alter a quotation which has been treated as having been accepted,
- take the initiative in ascertaining the facts and the law related to the dispute,
- instruct a Party to provide further information related to the dispute within a stated time and
- instruct a Party to take any other action which he considers necessary to reach his decision and to do so within a stated time

COMMUNICATIONS SHARED

W2.3(6)
A communication between a Party and the *Adjudicator* is communicated to the other Party at the same time

PARTY NOT COMPLYING

W2.3(5)
If a Party does not comply with any instruction within the time stated by the *Adjudicator*, the *Adjudicator* may continue the adjudication and make his decision based upon the information and evidence he has received

ADJUDICATOR CONTINUES?

W2.3(5)
Does the *Adjudicator* continue?

NO → **APPOINT NEW ADJUDICATOR** → B sheet 1

YES

ADJUDICATOR'S ASSESSMENT

W2.3(7)
If the *Adjudicator's* decision includes assessment of additional cost or delay caused to the *Contractor*, he makes his assessment in the same way as a CE is assessed

COMPENSATION EVENT ASSESSED

Does the *Adjudicator* make such an assessment?

YES → FC 63 Assessing CE

NO

ADJUDICATOR'S DECISION → A sheet 5

Flow chart W2 Sheet 4 of 6
Dispute resolution procedure W2

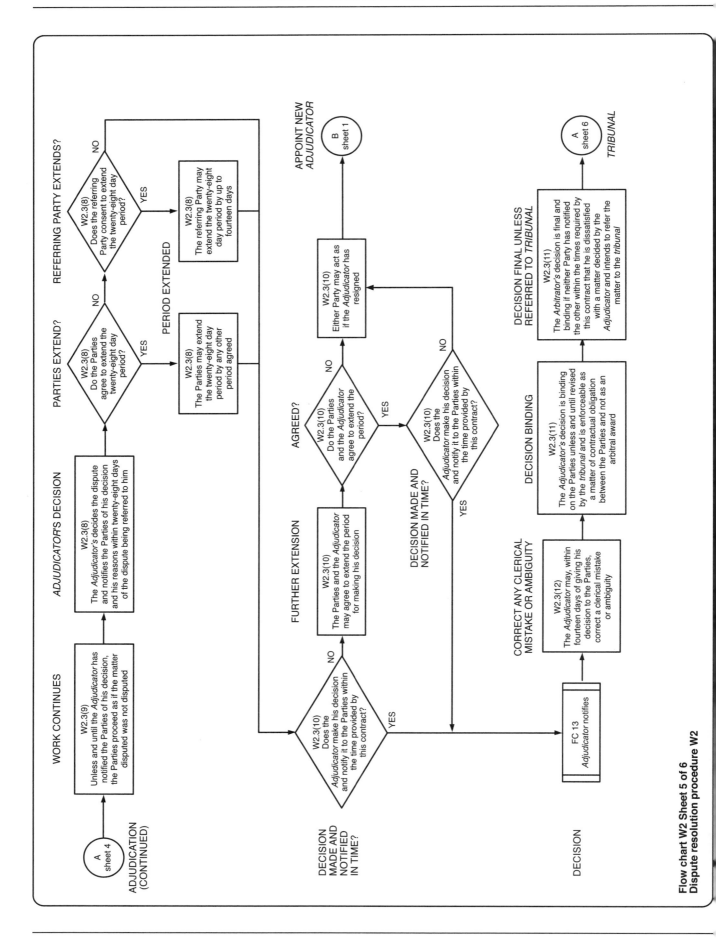

ADJUDICATION
(CONTINUED)

A
sheet 4

WORK CONTINUES

W2.3(9)
Unless and until the *Adjudicator* has notified the Parties of his decision, the Parties proceed as if the matter disputed was not disputed

ADJUDICATOR'S DECISION

W2.3(8)
The *Adjudicator's* decides the dispute and notifies the Parties of his decision and his reasons within twenty-eight days of the dispute being referred to him

PARTIES EXTEND?

W2.3(8)
Do the Parties agree to extend the twenty-eight day period?

NO / YES

REFERRING PARTY EXTENDS?

W2.3(8)
Does the referring Party consent to extend the twenty-eight day period?

NO / YES

PERIOD EXTENDED

W2.3(8)
The Parties may extend the twenty-eight day period by any other period agreed

W2.3(8)
The referring Party may extend the twenty-eight day period by up to fourteen days

APPOINT NEW
ADJUDICATOR

B
sheet 1

DECISION MADE AND
NOTIFIED IN TIME?

W2.3(10)
Does the *Adjudicator* make his decision and notify it to the Parties within the time provided by this contract?

NO / YES

FURTHER EXTENSION

W2.3(10)
The Parties and the *Adjudicator* may agree to extend the period for making his decision

AGREED?

W2.3(10)
Do the Parties and the *Adjudicator* agree to extend the period?

NO / YES

W2.3(10)
Either Party may act as if the *Adjudicator* has resigned

DECISION MADE AND
NOTIFIED IN TIME?

W2.3(10)
Does the *Adjudicator* make his decision and notify it to the Parties within the time provided by this contract?

YES / NO

DECISION

FC 13
Adjudicator notifies

CORRECT ANY CLERICAL
MISTAKE OR AMBIGUITY

W2.3(12)
The *Adjudicator* may, within fourteen days of giving his decision to the Parties, correct a clerical mistake or ambiguity

DECISION BINDING

W2.3(11)
The *Adjudicator's* decision is binding on the Parties unless and until revised by the *tribunal* and is enforceable as a matter of contractual obligation between the Parties and not as an arbitral award

DECISION FINAL UNLESS
REFERRED TO *TRIBUNAL*

W2.3(11)
The *Arbitrator's* decision is final and binding if neither Party has notified the other within the times required by this contract that he is dissatisfied with a matter decided by the *Adjudicator* and intends to refer the matter to the *tribunal*

A
sheet 6

TRIBUNAL

Flow chart W2 Sheet 5 of 6
Dispute resolution procedure W2

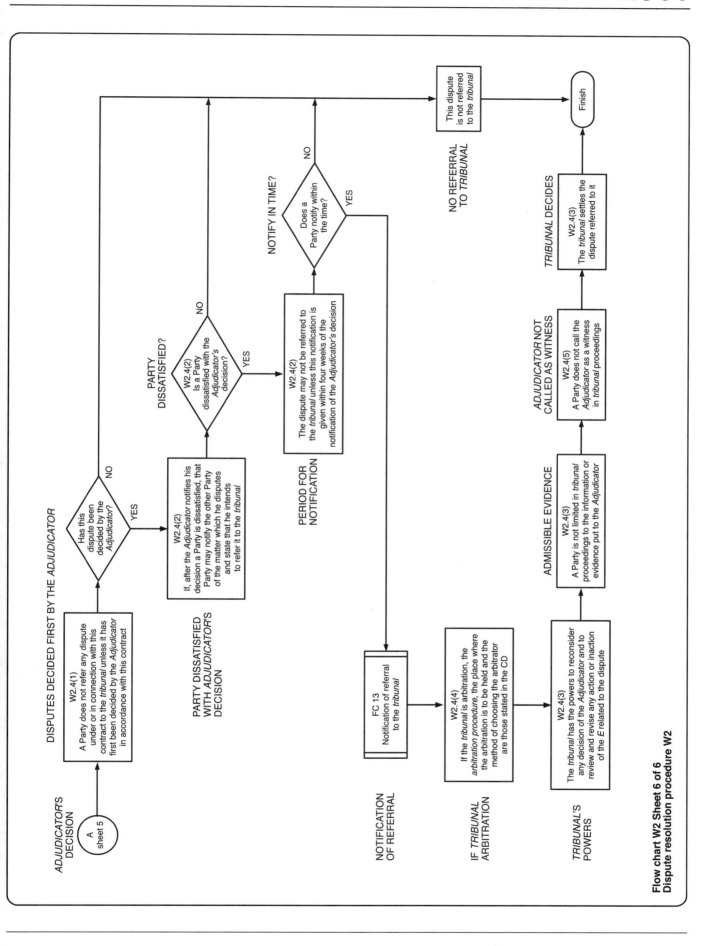

Flow chart W2 Sheet 6 of 6
Dispute resolution procedure W2

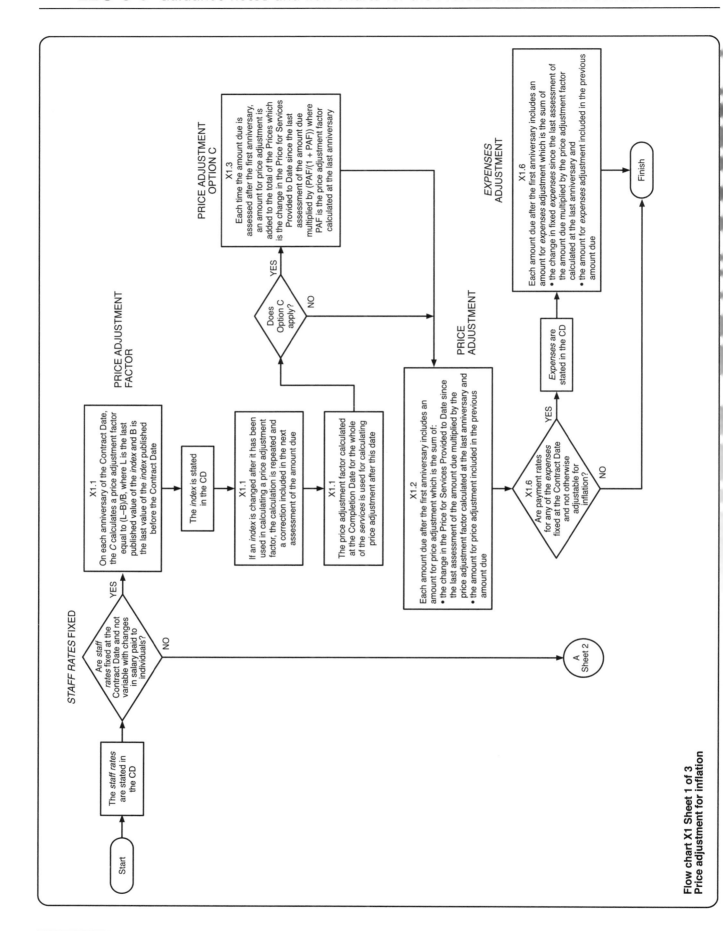

STAFF RATES FIXED

Start

The *staff rates* are stated in the CD

Are *staff rates* fixed at the Contract Date and not variable with changes in salary paid to individuals?

YES →

NO → A Sheet 2

PRICE ADJUSTMENT FACTOR

X1.1
On each anniversary of the Contract Date, the *C* calculates a price adjustment factor equal to (L–B)/B, where L is the last published value of the *index* and B is the last value of the *index* published before the Contract Date

X1.1
The *index* is stated in the CD

X1.1
If an *index* is changed after it has been used in calculating a price adjustment factor, the calculation is repeated and a correction included in the next assessment of the amount due

X1.1
The price adjustment factor calculated at the Completion Date for the whole of the *services* is used for calculating price adjustment after this date

Does Option C apply?

YES →

NO →

PRICE ADJUSTMENT OPTION C

X1.3
Each time the amount due is assessed after the first anniversary, an amount for price adjustment is added to the total of the Prices which is the change in the Price for Services Provided to Date since the last assessment of the amount due multiplied by (PAF/(1 + PAF)) where PAF is the price adjustment factor calculated at the last anniversary

PRICE ADJUSTMENT

X1.2
Each amount due after the first anniversary includes an amount for price adjustment which is the sum of:
• the change in the Price for Services Provided to Date since the last assessment of the amount due multiplied by the price adjustment factor calculated at the last anniversary and
• the amount for price adjustment included in the previous amount due

EXPENSES ADJUSTMENT

X1.6
Are payment rates for any of the *expenses* fixed at the Contract Date and not otherwise adjustable for inflation?

YES → *Expenses* are stated in the CD

NO →

X1.6
Each amount due after the first anniversary includes an amount for *expenses* adjustment which is the sum of
• the change in fixed *expenses* since the last assessment of the amount due multiplied by the price adjustment factor calculated at the last anniversary and
• the amount for *expenses* adjustment included in the previous amount due

Finish

Flow chart X1 Sheet 1 of 3
Price adjustment for inflation

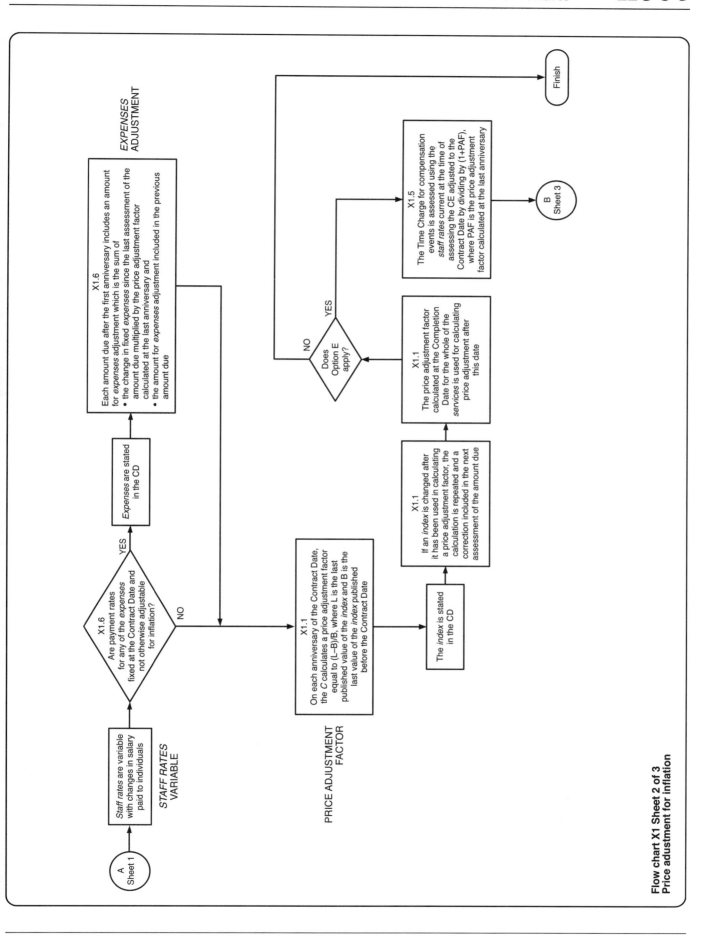

EXPENSES ADJUSTMENT

X1.6
Each amount due after the first anniversary includes an amount for *expenses* adjustment which is the sum of
• the change in fixed *expenses* since the last assessment of the amount due multiplied by the price adjustment factor calculated at the last anniversary and
• the amount for *expenses* adjustment included in the previous amount due

Expenses are stated in the CD

X1.6
Are payment rates for any of the *expenses* fixed at the Contract Date and not otherwise adjustable for inflation?

STAFF RATES VARIABLE

Staff rates are variable with changes in salary paid to individuals

A Sheet 1

YES

NO

PRICE ADJUSTMENT FACTOR

X1.1
On each anniversary of the Contract Date, the C calculates a price adjustment factor equal to (L–B)/B, where L is the last published value of the *index* and B is the last published value of the *index* published before the Contract Date

The *index* is stated in the CD

X1.1
If an *index* is changed after it has been used in calculating a price adjustment factor, the calculation is repeated and a correction included in the next assessment of the amount due

X1.1
The price adjustment factor calculated at the Completion Date for the whole of the *services* is used for calculating price adjustment after this date

Does Option E apply?

NO

YES

X1.5
The Time Charge for compensation events is assessed using the *staff rates* current at the time of assessing the CE adjusted to the Contract Date by dividing by (1+PAF), where PAF is the price adjustment factor calculated at the last anniversary

Finish

B Sheet 3

Flow chart X1 Sheet 2 of 3
Price adjustment for inflation

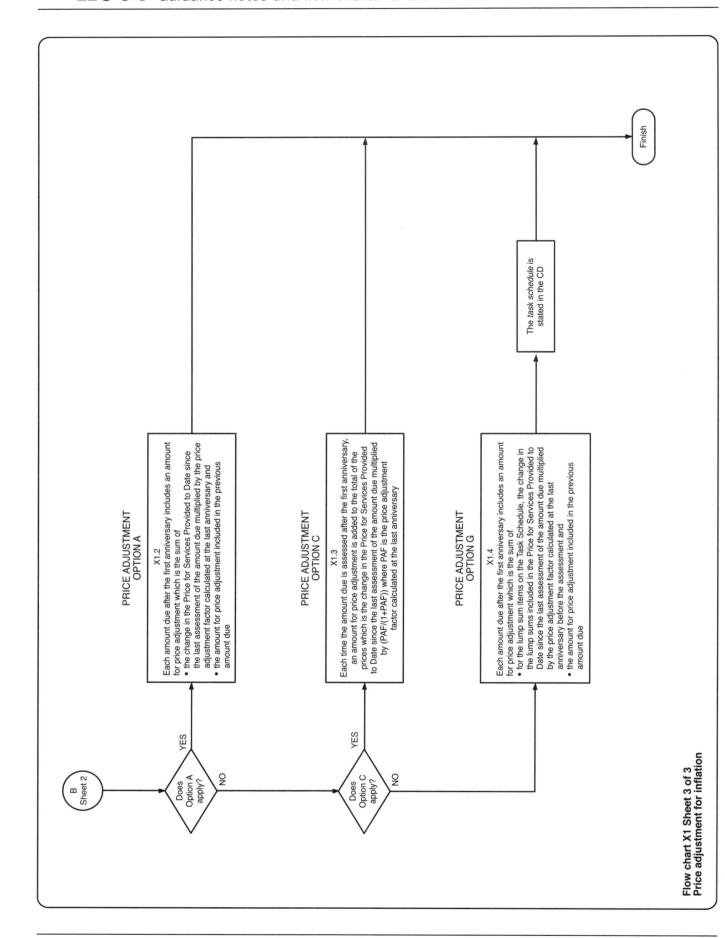

PRICE ADJUSTMENT
OPTION A

X1.2

Each amount due after the first anniversary includes an amount for price adjustment which is the sum of
• the change in the Price for Services Provided to Date since the last assessment of the amount due multiplied by the price adjustment factor calculated at the last anniversary and
• the amount for price adjustment included in the previous amount due

PRICE ADJUSTMENT
OPTION C

X1.3

Each time the amount due is assessed after the first anniversary, an amount for price adjustment is added to the total of the prices which is the change in the Price for Services Provided to Date since the last assessment of the amount due multiplied by (PAF/(1+PAF)) where PAF is the price adjustment factor calculated at the last anniversary

PRICE ADJUSTMENT
OPTION G

X1.4

Each amount due after the first anniversary includes an amount for price adjustment which is the sum of
• for the lump sum items on the Task Schedule, the change in the lump sums included in the Price for Services Provided to Date since the last assessment of the amount due multiplied by the price adjustment factor calculated at the last anniversary before the assessment and
• the amount for price adjustment included in the previous amount due

The *task schedule* is stated in the CD

B
Sheet 2

Does Option A apply? — YES
NO

Does Option C apply? — YES
NO

Finish

Flow chart X1 Sheet 3 of 3
Price adjustment for inflation

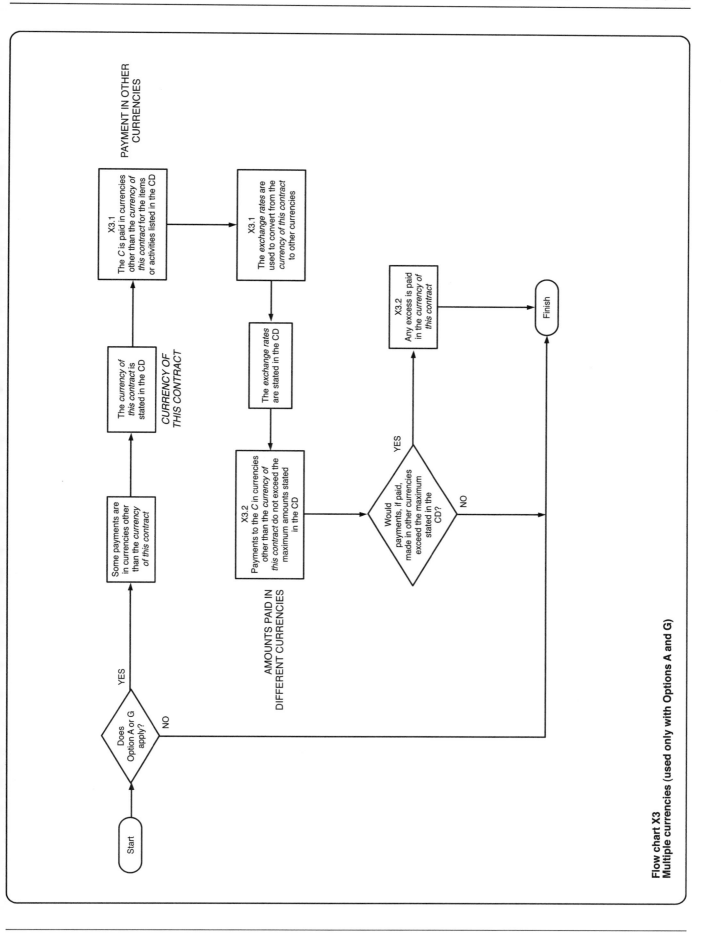

PAYMENT IN OTHER CURRENCIES

X3.1

The *C* is paid in currencies other than the *currency of this contract* for the items or activities listed in the CD

X3.1

The *exchange rates* are used to convert from the *currency of this contract* to other currencies

The *currency of this contract* is stated in the CD

CURRENCY OF THIS CONTRACT

The *exchange rates* are stated in the CD

X3.2

Any excess is paid in the *currency of this contract*

Finish

Some payments are in currencies other than the *currency of this contract*

YES

X3.2

Payments to the *C* in currencies other than the *currency of this contract* do not exceed the maximum amounts stated in the CD

AMOUNTS PAID IN DIFFERENT CURRENCIES

Would payments, if paid, made in other currencies exceed the maximum stated in the CD?

YES

NO

Does Option A or G apply?

NO

Start

Flow chart X3
Multiple currencies (used only with Options A and G)

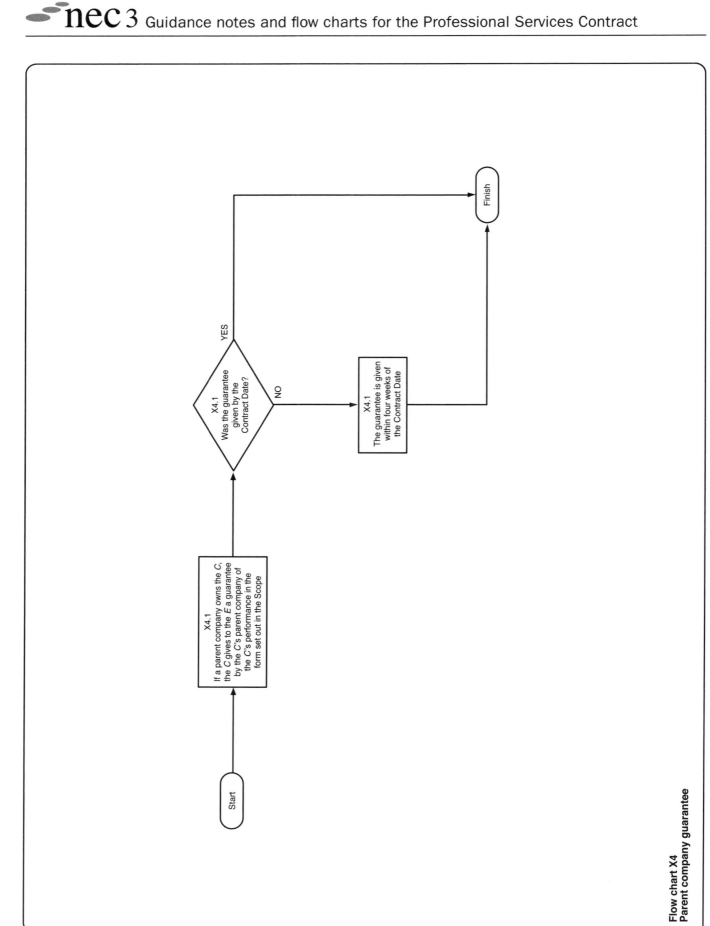

Flow chart X4
Parent company guarantee

Start

X4.1
If a parent company owns the C, the C gives to the E a guarantee by the C's parent company of the C's performance in the form set out in the Scope

X4.1
Was the guarantee given by the Contract Date?

YES

NO

X4.1
The guarantee is given within four weeks of the Contract Date

Finish

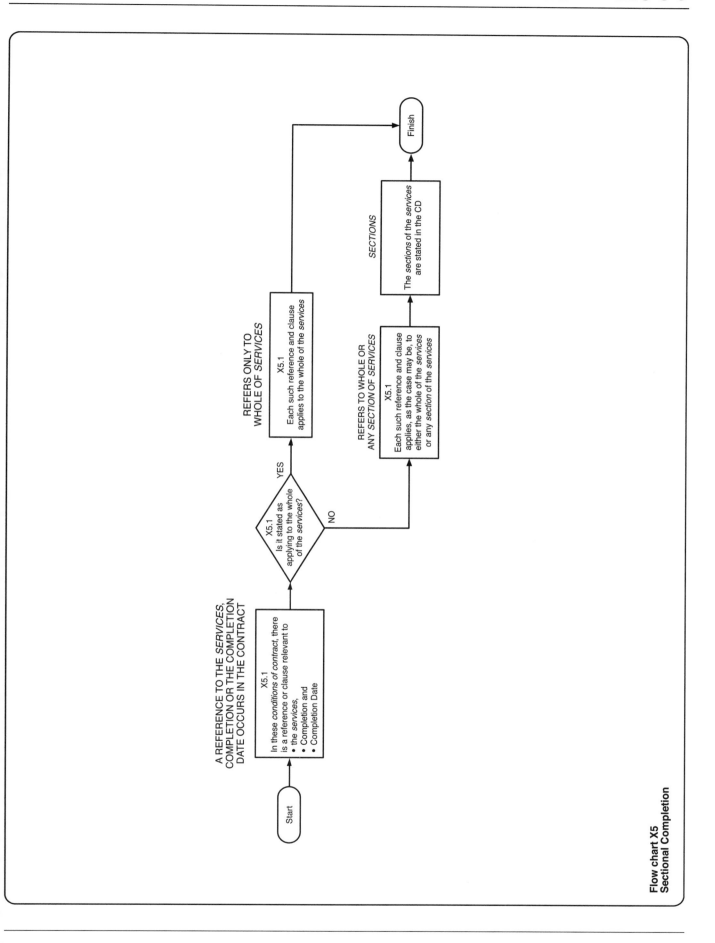

Start

A REFERENCE TO THE *SERVICES*,
COMPLETION OR THE COMPLETION
DATE OCCURS IN THE CONTRACT

X5.1
In these *conditions of contract*, there
is a reference or clause relevant to
• the *services*,
• Completion and
• Completion Date

X5.1
Is it stated as
applying to the whole
of the *services*?

YES

REFERS ONLY TO
WHOLE OF *SERVICES*

X5.1
Each such reference and clause
applies to the whole of the *services*

NO

REFERS TO WHOLE OR
ANY *SECTION* OF *SERVICES*

X5.1
Each such reference and clause
applies, as the case may be, to
either the whole of the *services*
or any *section* of the *services*

SECTIONS

The *sections* of the *services*
are stated in the CD

Finish

Flow chart X5
Sectional Completion

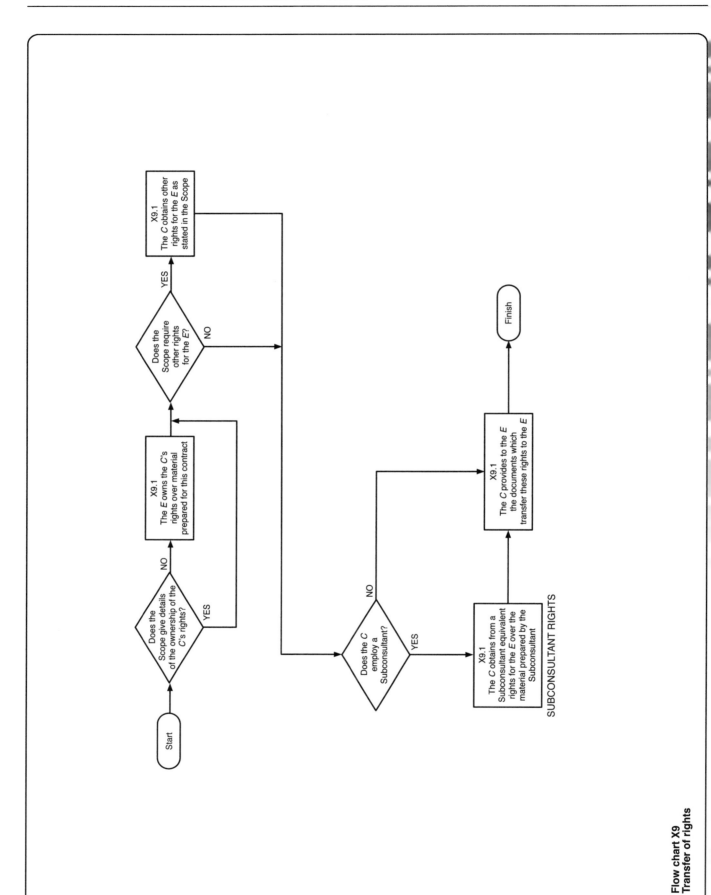

Flow chart X9
Transfer of rights

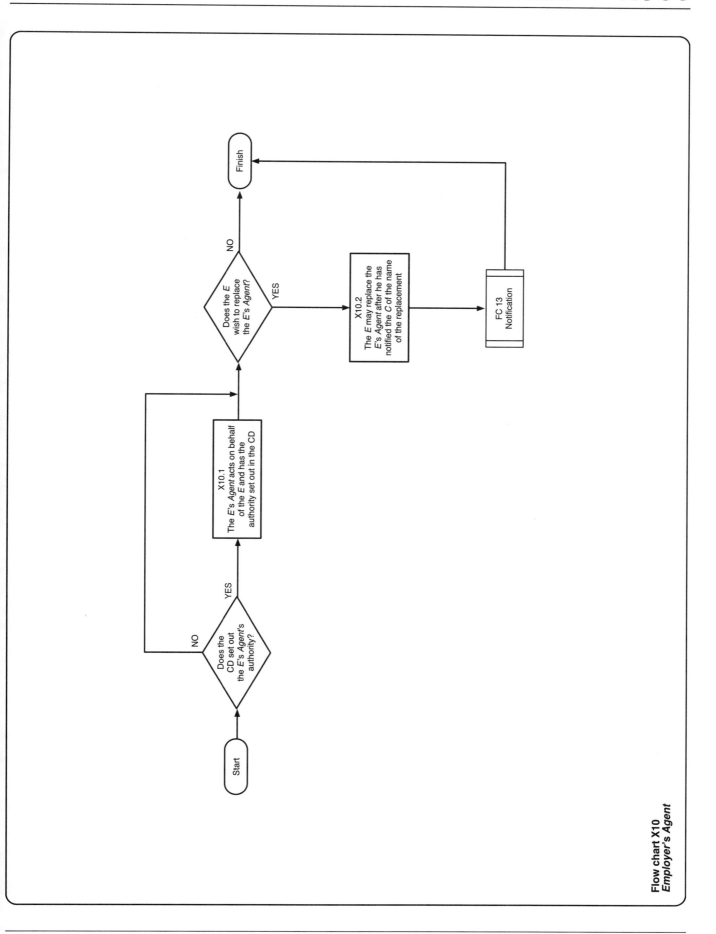

Flow chart X10
Employer's Agent

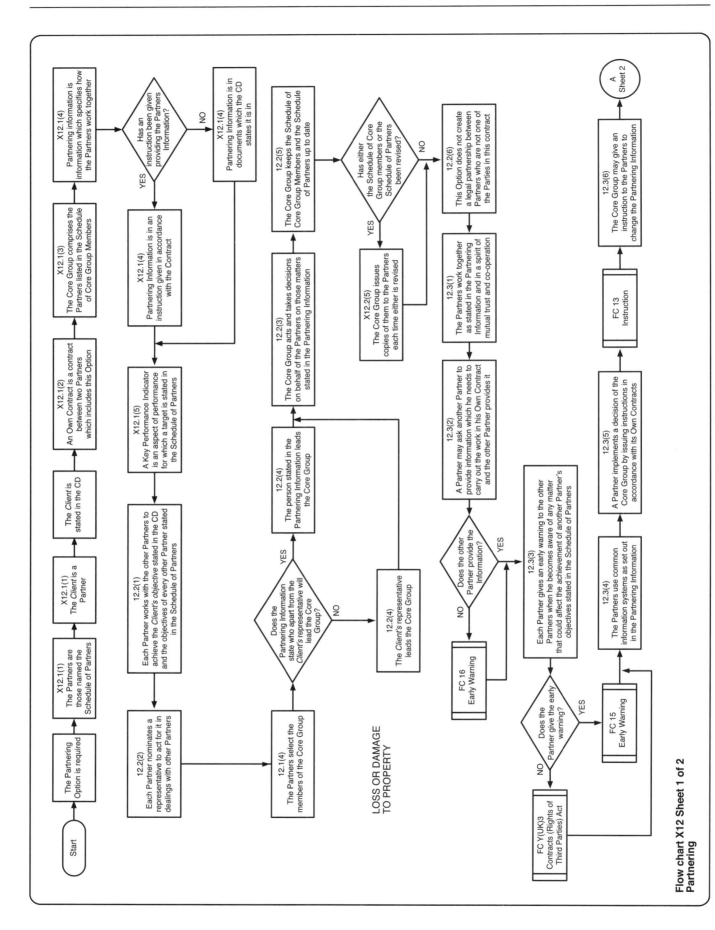

**Flow chart X12 Sheet 1 of 2
Partnering**

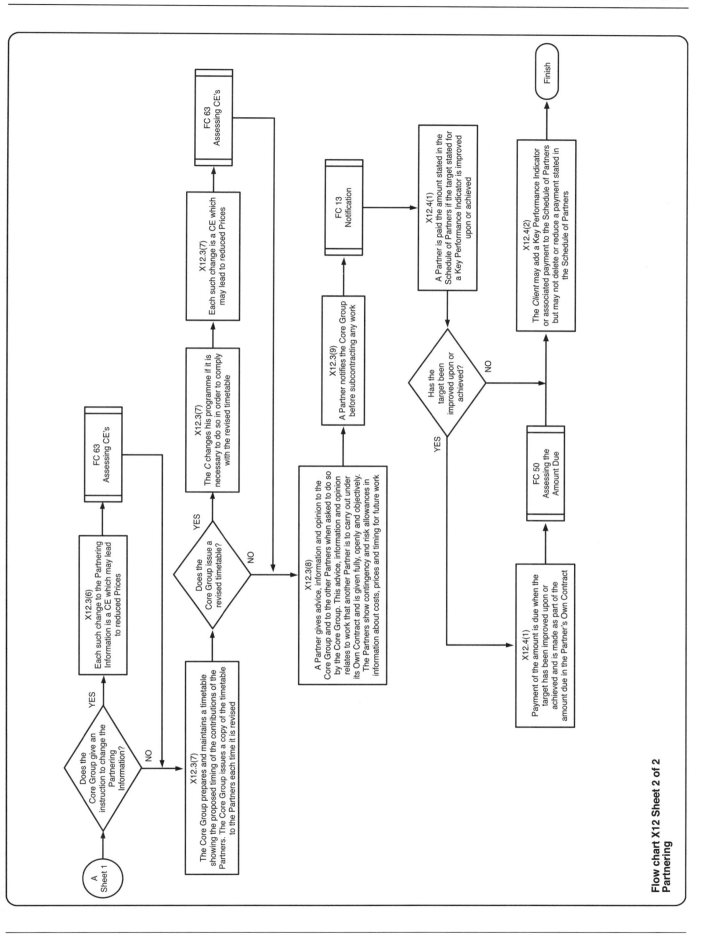

Flow chart X12 Sheet 2 of 2
Partnering

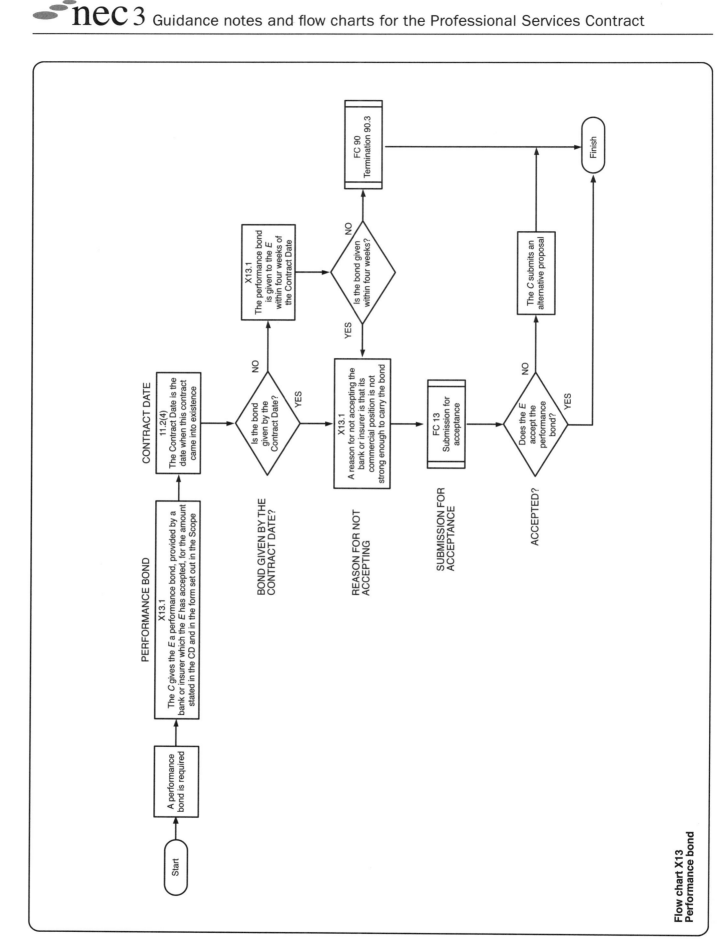

**Flow chart X13
Performance bond**

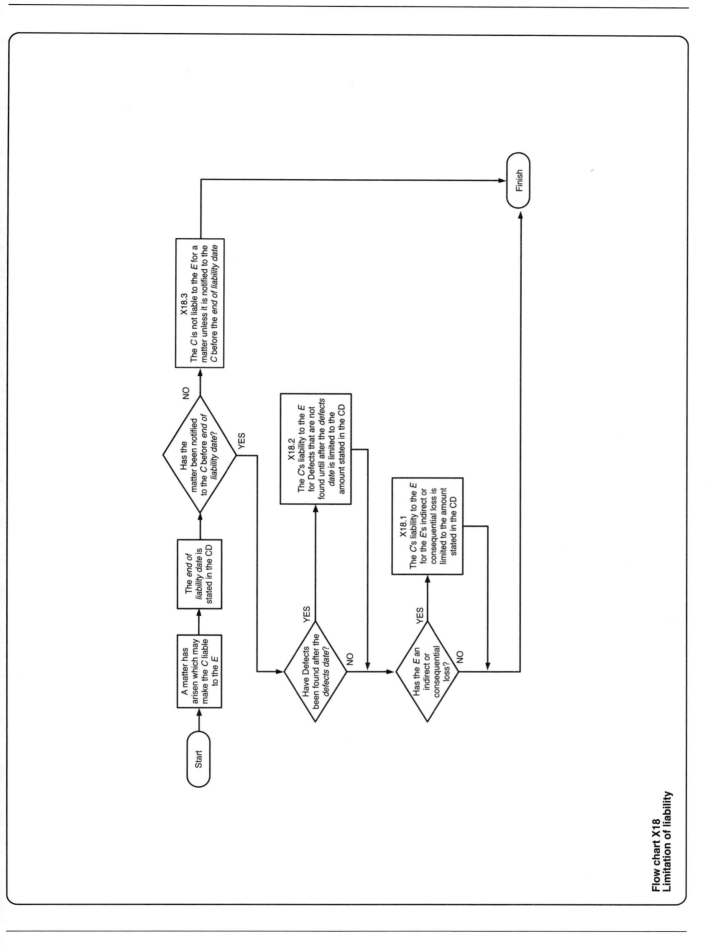

Flow chart X18
Limitation of liability

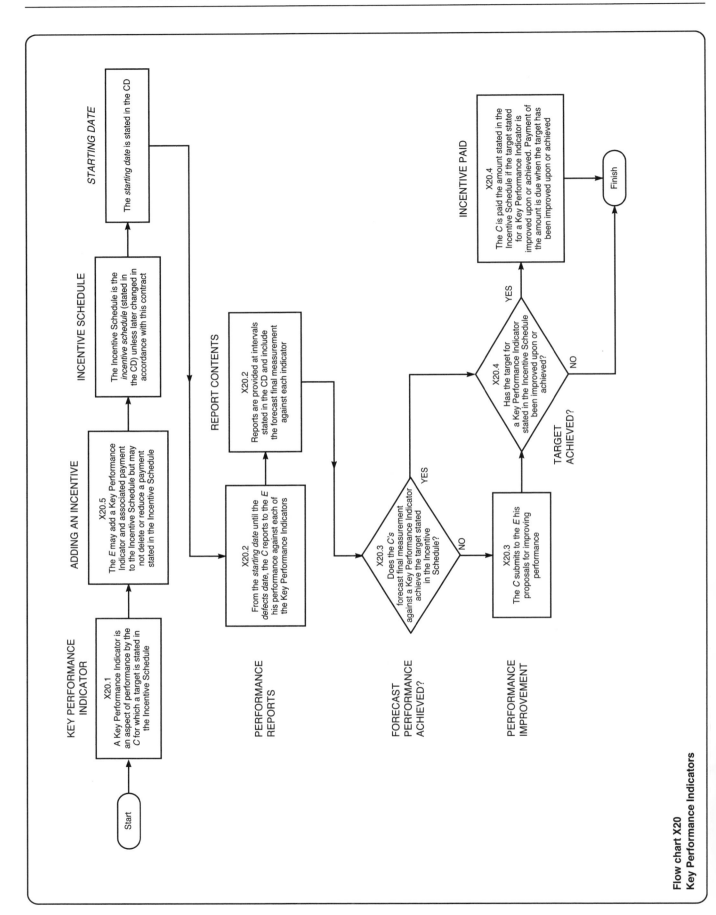

Flow chart X20
Key Performance Indicators

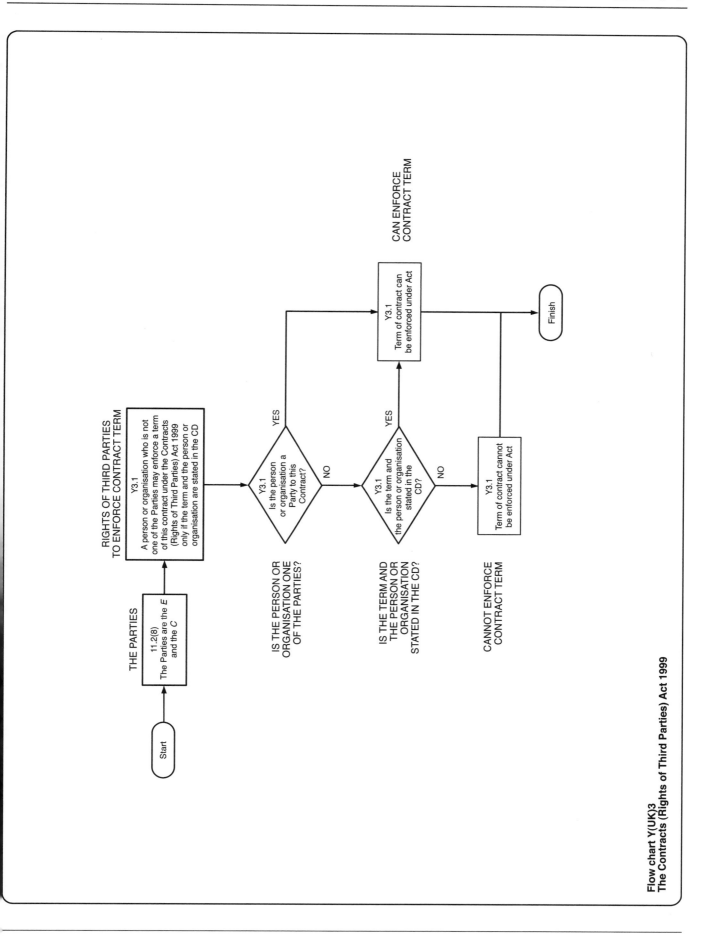

**RIGHTS OF THIRD PARTIES
TO ENFORCE CONTRACT TERM**

THE PARTIES

Start

11.2(8)
The Parties are the *E*
and the *C*

Y3.1
A person or organisation who is not
one of the Parties may enforce a term
of this contract under the Contracts
(Rights of Third Parties) Act 1999
only if the term and the person or
organisation are stated in the CD

**IS THE PERSON OR
ORGANISATION ONE
OF THE PARTIES?**

Y3.1
Is the person
or organisation a
Party to this
Contract?

NO

YES

**IS THE TERM AND
THE PERSON OR
ORGANISATION
STATED IN THE CD?**

Y3.1
Is the term and
the person or organisation
stated in the
CD?

NO

YES

**CANNOT ENFORCE
CONTRACT TERM**

Y3.1
Term of contract cannot
be enforced under Act

**CAN ENFORCE
CONTRACT TERM**

Y3.1
Term of contract can
be enforced under Act

Finish

**Flow chart Y(UK)3
The Contracts (Rights of Third Parties) Act 1999**

APPENDIX 1

Sample form of agreement

This agreement is made on the . . . . day of. . . . . .20 . . . .

between   •   . . . .(name)

                   of . . . .

                   (company/organisation) (the *Employer*)

and   •   . . . .(name)

                   of . . . .

                   (company/organisation) (the *Consultant*)

The *Employer* will pay the *Consultant* the amount due and carry out his duties in accordance with the *conditions of contract* identified in the Contract Data.

The *Consultant* will Provide the Services in accordance with the *conditions of contract* identified in the Contract Data.

Signed by . . . .

Name. . . . .

Position . . . .

On behalf of (*Employer*) . . . .

and . . . .

Name. . . . .

Position . . . .

On behalf of (*Consultant*) . . . .

Alternative if agreement is executed as a deed under English law

* When the *Employer* is an individual:

Executed as a deed by

. . . . (signed) Signature of Witness . . . .

. . . . (*Employer*) Name of Witness . . . .

* When the *Employer* is a company:

Executed as a deed by

. . . . (signed)

. . . . (name of Director)

. . . . (signed)

. . . . (name of Director or Company Secretary)

† When the *Consultant* is an individual or partnership:

Executed as a deed by

Name of individual or partner	Signature	Name of Witness	Signature
. . . .	. . . .	. . . .	. . . .
. . . .	. . . .	. . . .	. . . .
. . . .	. . . .	. . . .	. . . .
. . . .	. . . .	. . . .	. . . .

(Note: All partners to sign except where one is authorised as signatory by deed)

† When the *Consultant* is a Company

Executed as a deed by

. . . . (signed)

. . . . (name of Director)

. . . . (signed)

. . . . (name of Director or Company Secretary)

* Delete one of these
† Delete one of these

APPENDIX 2

Contract Data – worked example

Introduction

The following example shows how the Contract Data should be completed for a contract with a particular selection of decisions made by the *Employer*. It follows that not all the possible optional statements are included in the example. The guidance notes included under 'Basis of the appointment of a *Consultant*' are expanded by illustration.

The Contract Data for a particular contract must be prepared specifically for that contract. When re-typing or otherwise preparing the basic format, it is most important that the text printed in the PSC is not changed because it has been designed to read correctly with the relevant clauses in the PSC. The correct text for each statement is identified in the example by the font in this main text.

Contracts for the provision of professional services by a consultant are sometimes prepared as the outcome of negotiation during which the potential *Consultant* is already advising the *Employer* on the proposed contract between them. It is nevertheless important to recognise the three basic stages of this process, which become clearly separate when an employer is seeking bids in competition from several consultants. With respect to the preparation of the Contract Data for a contract under the PSC, these three stages are

a) *Employer* prepares an enquiry comprising a completed part one and a prepared format for part two,
b) bidding consultants prepare their offers by completing part two and
c) a contract is made between the *Employer* and the successful *Consultant*.

The example assumes that this process is followed, and the entries made at each stage are identified by the following fonts.

a) **European Grain plc**
b) *PM Services Ltd*
c) *Ms. 7. Arkwright*

The example also assumes that the following decisions have been made by the *Employer*

- main Option A has been chosen together with Option W2 and secondary Options X1, X2, X3, X4, X8, X9, X10, X11, Y(UK)2 and Z,

- the *completion date* for the whole of the *services*,

- a programme is not to be identified in the Contract Data,

- the period for payment of accounts is three weeks (as subclause 51.1),

- the amount to be paid for certain *expenses*, and the *Consultant* to quote for others,

- the *Consultant* is to provide additional insurances,

- the *Consultant*'s liability is not limited to the amount of his insurances and

- the *tribunal* is arbitration.

It is recommended that when an optional statement is used in Contract Data part one it is inserted under the appropriate section of the PSC, as illustrated in the example.

Part one – Data provided by the *Employer*

1 General
- The *conditions of contract* are the core clauses and the clauses for main Option **A**, dispute resolution Option **W2** and secondary Options **X1, X2, X3, X4, X8, X9, X10, X11, Y(UK)2 and Z** of the NEC3 Professional Services Contract (June 2005).

> Choose a main Option and the secondary Options appropriate to the contract, which must be compatible with the chosen main Option. See GNs on 'Contract strategy' and 'Basis of the appointment of a *Consultant*'.

> The *Employer*'s legal name.

- The *Employer* is

  Name   **European Grain plc**

  Address   **Long Acre Industrial Estate**
                Spearshead
                Bristol BS8 2LR
                Tel 01234 567890   Fax 01234 678905.

> *Employer*'s postal address (subclause 13.2) including postcode, telephone and facsimile numbers for the purpose of the contract (not necessarily the registered address).

- The *Adjudicator* is

  Name   *Ms. J. Arkwright*

  Address   *Solva and Smith Project Management*
                Meadow House, Goode Road
                Exeter EX8 6LN
                tel 01567 23456   fax 01567 78901.

> Leave blank until the Parties have jointly agreed an appointee. At Contract Date, state the *Adjudicator*'s name, postal address with postcode, telephone and facsimile numbers for the purpose of the contract. See GN on subclause W2.2(1).

- The *services* are

  Project management of extensions to unloading and distribution facilities at Long Acre Works.

> Describe the *services* briefly for their general identification.

> State references of the documents containing the Scope. See GN on 'Basis of the appointment of a *Consultant*' and Table 2.

- The Scope is in

  Document ref XX90.

- The *language of this contract* is **English.**

> Subclause 13.1.

- The *law of the contract* is the law of **England and Wales.**

> Subclause 12.2.

> GN on subclause 13.3.

- The *period for reply* is **2** weeks.

- The *period for retention* is **2** years following Completion or earlier termination.

> GN on subclause 13.6.

- The *Adjudicator nominating body* is

  Institution of Civil Engineers.

- The *tribunal* is **arbitration.**

- The *arbitration procedure* is **the latest edition of the ICE Arbitration Procedure.**

- The place where arbitration is to be held is **London.**

- The person or organisation who will choose an arbitrator
  - if the Parties cannot agree a choice or
  - if the *arbitration procedure* does not state who selects an arbitrator
  is **Institution of Civil Engineers.**

- The following matters will be included in the Risk Register
  As shown in Document ref XYZ dated 20 June 2005.

- The *additional conditions of contract* are **Clauses Z1 to Z6 as in document Grain Additional GA 12 dated 20 June 2005.**

> If Option Z is used, refer to GN on Option Z and state the conditions here with reference numbers using prefix 'Z'.

2 The Parties' main responsibilities

- The *Employer* provides access to the following persons, places and things

GN on subclause 25.2.

access to	access date
Long acre works and *Employer*'s *Agent*	5 July 2005.

- The *Employer's Agent* is

Name	Mr. E. X. E. Cutive
Address	Long Acre Industrial Estate
	Spearshead
	Bristol BS8 2LR.

If Option X10 is used.

See GN on Option X10.

If Option X10 is used.

See GN on Option X10.

- The authority of the *Employer's Agent* is

all actions by the *Employer* stated in this contract.

- The *collateral warranty agreements* are

If Option X8 is used, the details of any *collateral warranty agreements* should be referred to here and appended to the Contract Data.

See GN on Option X8.

Agreement reference	Third party
NXT/Door-1	Adjacent Properties plc.

3 Time

- The *starting date* is **5 July 2005.**

GN on subclause 31.2.

- The *Consultant* is to submit a first programme for acceptance within **3** weeks of the Contract Date.

If no programme is to be identified in part two of the Contract Data. See GN on subclause 31.1.

- The *completion date* for the whole of the *services* is

30 June 2006.

If the Employer decides *completion date*.

GN on subclause 30.1.

4 Quality

- The quality policy statement and quality plan are provided within **3** weeks of the Contract Date.

Subclause 40.2.

- The *defects date* is **26** weeks after Completion of the whole of the *services*.

Subclause 41.1.

5 Payment

- The *assessment interval* is **a calendar month.**

- The *currency of this contract* is **pounds sterling (£).**

Can be any period but preferably not longer than five weeks. See GN on subclause 50.1.

- The *interest rate is* **2** % per annum above the **base lending rate of Lloyds Bank plc.**

GN on subclause 51.5.

- The *expenses* stated by the *Employer* are

If the *Employer* states any *expenses* and the amount to be paid.

See GN on subclause 50.3.

item	amount
car mileage	40p per mile
rail travel	standard class fare.

- The *Consultant* prepares forecasts of the total *expenses* at intervals no longer than **12** weeks.

- The *Employer* will pay for the items or activities listed below in the currencies stated

GN on clause 52.

items and activities	other currency	total maximum payment in the currency
Consultancy on design of loading equipment	Euros	Euros 30,000.

If Option X3 is used.

See GN on Option X3.

- The *exchange rates* are those published in

Financial Times on **1 June 2005.**

- The *index* is **the Retail Prices Index.**

If Option X1 is used.

See GN on Option X1.

6 Compensation events

- The *law of the project* is **Law of England and Wales.**

If Option X2 is used.

See GN on Option X2.

8 Indemnity, insurance and liability

- The amounts of insurance and the periods for which the *Consultant* maintains insurance are

event	cover	period following Completion of the whole of the *services* or earlier termination
failure of the *Consultant* to use the skill and care normally used by professionals providing services similar to the *services*	**£5m** in respect of each claim, without limit to the number of claims	**6 years**
death of or bodily injury to a person (not an employee of the *Consultant*) or loss of or damage to property resulting from an action or failure to take action by the *Consultant*	**£5m** in respect of each claim, without limit to the number of claims	**12 months**
death of or bodily injury to employees of the *Consultant* arising out of and in the course of their employment in connection with this contract	**£2m** in respect of each claim, without limit to the number of claims	**12 months**

GN on subclause 81.1.

GN on subclause 81.1.

GN on subclause 81.1.

- The *Employer* provides the following insurances

| **Liability for loss of or damage to property (except survey equipment) provided by the *Employer* for the use of the *Consultant*.** | **The replacement cost until the property is returned to the *Employer*.** |

GN on subclause 82.1.

- The *Consultant*'s total liability to the *Employer* for all matters arising under or in connection with this contract, other than excluded matters, is limited to
  the amount of the *Consultant*'s professional indemnity insurance cover

- The *Consultant* provides these additional insurances

  1. Insurance against **liability for loss of or damage to survey equipment provided by the *Employer***
     Cover is **replacement cost**
     Period of cover **until all the equipment is returned to the *Employer***
     Deductibles are **nil**

If the *Consultant* is to provide additional insurances see GN on subclause 81.1.

Part two – Data provided by the *Consultant*

- The *Consultant* is

Name	**PM Services Ltd**
Address	**Enterprise Way**
	Bristol
	BS90 6PM.

Bidding consultant to state legal name and postal address (with postcode) for the purpose of the contract.

See subclause 13.2.

- The *key persons* are

Name	**Ms. K. Smithson**
Job	**Project Manager**
Responsibilities	**In charge of the project**
Qualifications	**MSc, MIMechE**
Experience	**3 years as Project Manager, 4 years as Assistant PM.**

Name	**Mr. V. Green**
Job	**Chief Designer**
Responsibilities	**Supervising design of plant**
Qualifications	**PhD, FICE**
Experience	**10 years design of process plants.**

- The *staff rates* are

name/designation	rate
Ms. K. Smithson (PM)	**£75 per hour**
Mr. V. Green (Chief Designer)	**£65 per hour**
Mr. W. Jones (Estimator)	**£60 per hour**
Ms. J. Brown (Planner)	**£60 per hour**
Assistants	**£35 per hour.**

Bidding consultant to quote *staff rates* for the different categories (or names) of staff.

See GN on subclause 11.2(13).

- The *expenses* stated by the *Consultant* are

item	amount
Subsistence (as authorised away from home address)	**£80 per night**
Printing of drawings	**£5.50 per A1 size print.**

If the *Consultant* states the *expenses* and the amount to be paid. (These can be in addition to those stated by the *Employer* in the Contract Data part one.)

See GN on subclause 50.3

- The following matters will be included in the Risk Register
  As shown in Document ref RR1.

- The *Employer* provides access to the following persons, places and things

access to	access date
Designers of loading equipment	**12 July 2005.**

GN on subclause 25.2

- The *activity schedule* is **AS 1.**

If Option A or C is used, bidding consultant to state reference of his priced *activity schedule*.

See GN on *activity schedule*.